T24019

F
WAN

Wang, An-i.

Baotown

$17.45

DATE		
JAN/18-9 1990		
FEB 23 1990	OCT 6 1992	
MAR 1 5 1990		
JUL 0 5 1990	MAY 1 1993	
	JAN 1 9 1999	
JUL 2 6 1990	AUG 2 5 1999	
AUG 0 7 1990		
SEP 1 5 1990	12-28	
OCT 1 5 1990		
JUL 0 7 1992		

BAOTOWN

Wang Anyi

BAOTOWN

TRANSLATED BY MARTHA AVERY

W · W · Norton & Company
New York   London

Copyright © 1985 by Wang Anyi
Translation copyright © 1989 by Martha Avery
First American Edition, 1989.

Printed in the United States of America.

Library of Congress Cataloging-in-Publication Data
Wang, Anyi.
    [Hsiao Pao chuang.   English]
    Baotown / by Wang Anyi; translated by Martha Avery. — 1st ed.
        p.   cm.
    Translation of: Hsiao Pao chuang.
    I. Title.
PL2919.A58H713   1989
895.1′35—dc19   89–2882

ISBN 0-393-02711-2

W. W. Norton & Company, Inc.,
500 Fifth Avenue, New York, N.Y. 10110
W. W. Norton & Company Ltd.,
37 Great Russell Street, London WC1B 3NU
1 2 3 4 5 6 7 8 9 0

PREFACE

Seven days and seven nights of rain, rain that turned the day-time into night. And then the flood, pounding over Bao Mountain, turning the dark into a stretching sheet of white.

The people of Baotown saw the wall of whiteness rolling towards them, saw it and tried to run. Seven days of rain had softened the earth: as each foot came down it sank up to the calf. The wave of white rolled on inexorably, a solid mass capped with splashes of spray.

Thatched houses collapsed, sturdy, deep-rooted trees were knocked over like toys.

Children did not cry, mothers did not call, chickens did not fly, dogs did not move, the sky was not black, the earth was not white. All was still.

The sky was gone, the earth was gone. The sparrows were silent.

In time – a moment or a century – a tree floated to the surface, painting a line between heaven and earth. A dark brushstroke defining the top of the water. On it coiled a solitary snake.

Baotown's founder had been a court official. Dispatched by

the Dragon Throne,* he had been ordered to stop the floods. In nine hundred and ninety-nine days, with nine thousand, nine hundred and ninety-nine men, he built what would be known as Bao Dam.

This dam enclosed a basin of ninety-nine thousand, nine hundred and ninety-nine *mou*† of fertile land, and when it was finished the area enjoyed a few years of peace. One perverse year the rain fell for seven weeks. After forty-nine days and nights the water came over the dam, pouring into the basin, covering all those *mou* of good land. The dam was too strong and there was nowhere for the water to escape: when the rain stopped the basin had become a lake.

It was three years before the lake bottom dried out. The founder of Baotown was dismissed, but his past diligence kept the Dragon Throne from sentencing him to death. Remorseful, the founder tried to figure out where he had gone wrong – he had only wanted to build a solid dam for the people. Finally he took his wife and children to the lowest land under Bao Dam, to live there in atonement for his wrongdoing. A small town slowly grew from this unfortunate start, until it numbered several hundred people.

Weeds flourished in the soggy basin. Swarms of locusts flew up from the weeds, hiding the sun and darkening the day. A flood was still most feared, however, and the only way to stop a flood was to keep mending the dam. Shovel by shovel, mud went up to the top: the sight of a high dam made people feel there was something solid to rely on. As the years went by the dam became taller and broader, until later generations began to call it Bao Mountain. The land that was encircled by Bao Mountain came to be known as The Lake. While other people

---

* The Emperor of China.

† A *mou* is a Chinese measure of land equal to .1647 acres. When land was redistributed in 1978–9, each individual received 1.7 *mou*, or slightly more than one-quarter of an acre.

talked of 'going down to work in the fields', people in Bao-town said 'going down to work in The Lake'.

Bao Mountain was not that high, nor was the land that low, but the mountain locked it in, dividing a small world inside from what was far away and on the outside.

All this, of course, is legend. It forms the basis of what later generations came to call the old stories. These later generations passed the stories on to their children, and in time they sprouted tendrils and fresh leaves.

For example, there was the embellishment about direct lineage to Yu.* The founder of Baotown was said to be his descendent, although this founder lacked the spirit of Yu. Everyone knew that only three days after taking a wife, Yu had left his home to control the floods; three times after that he passed his door without going in. When his wife bore a son whose cries he could hear, he still worked with such resolve that he did not return home. In contrast, the founder of Baotown sired three sons and a daughter while building his dam – legend said that he was later punished by the flood.

Naturally, this is just a tall tale, nothing to believe. It is only a story for one generation to tell the next.

---

* Yu was the reputed founder of the Xia dynasty (c.21–16 century BC)

BAOTOWN

CHAPTER 1

Bao Yanshan's wife was in labour, about to give birth on her bed at home. Big Dog, the son of Baotown's troop leader, ran shouting down to The Lake to find Yanshan. He came sauntering up, hands behind his back, hoe tucked under one arm, thinking what a common occurrence this had become. The seventh belly, no problem, he was thinking – she's just like an old mother hen dropping another egg. To have it come three months early was that much better: this time of year there was plenty to eat. But whether it was three months, or three days, or three hours, it was not worth getting excited about.

Several old men already sat outside his door, yawning as they commented, 'hasn't hit the earth yet'. Yanshan propped his hoe against the side of the house and squatted down too.

'Wheat coming up all right?' Bao Erye asked.

''Bout the same,' he answered.

The sound of a child crying came through the door. The wife of Yanshan's third brother pushed it open and yelled, 'It's a boy!'

'A boy – that's good.' Bao Erye said.

''Bout the same,' Yanshan answered.

'Aren't you coming in to take a look?' Third Brother's wife emerged again to call him.

Standing up, Yanshan settled his coat on his shoulders, straightened his back and went inside. In a minute he was out again.

'What do you think?' Bao Erye asked.

' 'Bout the same,' he answered.

'What name are you thinking of?'

Yanshan paused to think about that for a moment, then said, 'His proper name will be Bao Renping, but I reckon his nickname will be Dregs.'

'Dregs?'

'Dregs. This is going to be the last one.' He gave an embarrassed laugh as he explained, 'We didn't do too much to keep from having this one, you see.'

'It's got a good ring to it, anyway – Dregs!' Bao Erye nodded in approval.

Third Brother's wife appeared again, charging past Yanshan, yelling as she went, 'Man, I'm not having my sister eating sweet potato noodles for her month of confinement!' She disappeared, and soon returned carrying a pot of wheat noodles. She marched back into the room.

'Don't you all have wheat noodles here at home?' asked Bao Erye.

'What's it matter?' Yanshan laughed. 'My woman can make mama if she eats nothing but grass.' In Baotown they called a mother's milk 'mama'.

As they joked, Big Dog suddenly came running up, a sheaf of grass tied on to his back. 'Society has died!'

From a small thatched hut to the east they now heard the muffled cries of Bao Fifth Grandfather. Inside, the hut was full of old women, all noisily wiping eyes and blowing noses. Bao Fifth Grandfather was crying in a corner by himself.

'You old diehard,' he was snuffling to himself, 'why don't you kick the bucket too? You just keep on living, as if life never ends.

You end-of-the-liner,* what point is there to go on living now?'

His one and only grandson was lying stiff and straight, face already turning a waxy yellow. Since the previous year when the boy had contracted tuberculosis he had been spitting blood, spitting as hard as he could – spitting until his innards dried up and he died.

'When he got up he ate a bowl of porridge, and he said to me, "Grandpa, hold me so I can sit up – help me sit up a minute." I didn't stop him, and so he died!' Fifth Grandfather shuffled his feet around on the floor in helpless agony.

The old women sobbed.

The troop leader squeezed inside, knelt down beside Fifth Grandfather and tried to comfort him. 'Gramps, don't be upset. There's no way you're going to be an end-of-the-liner. Everyone in this town with a "ren"† in his name, everyone who grew up with Society is your grandson.'

'That's right.'

'That's right!' There was not a head in the room that did not nod in agreement.

'If any house has food in its pot, then your bowl is not going empty.'

'This old man isn't going to get food from someone else's pot!' Fifth Grandfather started up again.

'Gramps, why do you keep thinking the worst? Respect for older people isn't some kind of feudal ethic.'

Fifth Grandfather's crying subsided a little.

'Sure we have Socialism now, a New Society, but Gramps, even if you went back a hundred years in Baotown, you wouldn't find a single person who starved or froze to death, or anyone who wasn't taken care of by the others!'

---

* A person without descendants to carry on his name.

† In traditional China, all children of the same generation in a family were given the same or similar middle names. Since all the families of Baotown were closely related, their children all had the same middle name.

'That's right.'

Fifth Grandfather stopped snuffling and managed to answer, 'I'm just saying what a wretched life this is – now I've outlasted my own wife, my son and my grandson.'

'Don't say that, Gramps – life and death aren't up to us.' As the troop leader reasoned with him, Fifth Grandfather gradually calmed down.

CHAPTER 2

On the other side of Bao Mountain is a small place called Fengtown. In Fengtown lived a girl named Little Huitz. In 1960* she and her father headed north to beg for food – they walked out of town together, and two or three years later she came back, alone.

The father was gone, but a two-year-old boy had been added: the story was that he had been picked up along the road, so she called him Picked-Up and he called her Aunt.

In time, the whole town began to call her Aunt. She never married, just passed the days rearing Picked-Up. Aunt loved Picked-Up, loved him like her own son. She ate thin porridge while he ate thick; he wore new while she wore patched. Only once did anyone see her turn against him, and even then it was not for anything big. Picked-Up had come across a pedlar's

---

* In China 1960 was the start of the so-called 'Three Years of Natural Disaster', when millions starved as a direct result of the disastrous policies of the Great Leap Forward. 'Natural disasters' are still the official Chinese reason for the famine. It has been estimated that 20 million people died of starvation in 1961 alone.

5

drum somewhere or other, and he sat in the doorway shaking it and playing with it. Aunt's hand came whipping down and cuffed him on the ear. Picked-Up had broken plenty of better things and Aunt had never cared: was this drum made of gold or something?

That was one queer thing, and there was another. One day a group of wives were sitting around, taking in the sun and stitching soles of shoes. Picked-Up came over and buried his head in Aunt's breast, reaching out as he did so to lift the front of her loose gown. Aunt's face changed. She pushed him away, picked up her stool and walked off, leaving Picked-Up standing there behind. The ladies teased him then, saying, 'Want some mama? Go look for your own mother, that's just your Aunt, don't you know?'

Picked-Up wrinkled up his face and was going to cry, but did not.

Snide remarks began passing around the town, which were never addressed to Aunt directly, but often addressed to little Picked-Up.

'Picked-Up, that pedlar's drum of your Aunt's – find it for me. It won't hurt if I play with it awhile, eh!'

'Picked-Up, have you ever had any of your Aunt's mama?'

'Picked-Up, your Aunt . . .'

Although Picked-Up was small, he knew that what he was hearing was not good. Instead of asking Aunt about it, he kept stubbornly quiet. The queerer his tormentors found all this, the more they persisted in teasing him.

Picked-Up would look at them silently, then turn around without a word and go away. People began to suspect even more that these two – one big, one small – were harbouring some juicy secret together. So Picked-Up began to avoid people completely, keeping his distance from everyone except his Aunt.

Time passed, Aunt took care of Picked-Up and got them through. As she aged, no one cared to bring up the subject of relations any more. Picked-Up grew until he became a strong young man, with nine and a half cents as a regular wage.

6

They were still living in the one-room house built by Aunt's father – to get through the door, they had to bend over until they almost crawled on the ground. Inside it was dark except for the meagre light afforded by a 'window': two bricks removed from the wall. In winter they stuffed a wad of grass in this brick-hole, and in summer they pulled it out again.

Below the hearth was a cutting board, beside the cutting board a bed. On the bed was one woven bamboo sleeping mat, and on the mat one pillow and one quilt. Now that Picked-Up was grown, one pillow was not enough, so Aunt sewed up a cloth bag, stuffed it with wheat husks, and made another. Each head now slept on its own pillow: Aunt slept with her arms around Picked-Up's feet. As for Picked-Up, only with his feet safely tucked in Aunt's bosom could he feel at home and able to go to sleep.

One night in the early spring, Picked-Up felt hot and parched, suddenly wide awake and unable to sleep. His feet were resting in Aunt's bosom, warm, soft, warm and soft. Very gently, he moved his toes and found an even softer spot, even warmer – and now the skin on his head began to tingle. He did not dare move as he felt his heart begin to pound. A breeze came through the brick-hole, the grass outside was rustling.

He tried to move his toes again, away from that place, but instead his feet settled even deeper into its soft warmth. A new meaning had come to that familiar canyon – he knew for the first time where his feet had slept for fifteen years. He felt, moreover, that in the deepest reaches of that canyon, in the furthest part, there was another heart pounding. The wind blew gently through the brick-hole, softly sighing.

The next morning, Picked-Up kept his eyes lowered as he ate his porridge. He did not speak, and Aunt finally said, 'What's up with you? Something the matter?'

He did not answer. She went over to feel his head. He twisted his head and moved away.

At noon Aunt had the fire going for lunch long before she saw him coming home, carrying the frame for a summer bed.

She asked him where it came from: doggedly silent, he put his head down, pulling the rope hard as he began to make a netting for the frame.

That night Picked-Up slept by himself on a separate bed, head buried in the pillow, wrapped in a wad of old cotton rags. He was all curled up until some time towards the middle of the night, when he finally began to warm up and stretch out. He dreamed that his feet were in the warm canyon again, not knowing that his Aunt had put their one quilt on top of him. She slept alone in the clothes that she had on.

CHAPTER 3

Bao Renwen was pestering the old revolutionary, plaguing him with questions about his life. He wanted to write a novel, the title of which was to be: *A Tale of the Heroic Sons and Daughters of Bao Mountain*. Bao Yanrong had fought campaigns with the troops of Chen I. Many were the times he had looked death in the face. But he had little interest, these days, in the events of the past, although he still took his monthly veterans' stipend of nine yuan. He had even less interest in aggrandizing himself. His greatest concern was how to fill the many mouths of his family.

Seeing Bao Renwen with his everlasting notebook had brought Yanrong near the end of his patience. He would long ago have dismissed Renwen were it not for the young man's clever device of offering cigarettes: this promise of cigarettes thoroughly frustrated his resolve.

'Grandfather, when you were fighting at the Battle of Mengliang-gu* and your troop commander was killed in the

---

* Battle fought in Shandong in May 1947, in which General Chiang Kai-shek's troops were defeated by the Communists. According to the People's Republic of China the Kuomintang lost 32,000 men.

9

line of duty and you instinctively took over, leading the soldiers to victory – what were you feeling at that time, Grandfather?' Bao Renwen started his questioning.

'Wasn't thinking of anything, even of farting,' Bao Yanrong answered.

Bao Renwen tried to hide his disappointment and asked again. 'If you would try to remember, just think back, what were you thinking at that moment?'

Bao Yanrong drew deeply on his cigarette. 'Didn't have time to think. Brain was numb from the fighting, didn't have anything in it.'

'What motivation brought on that instinctive decision to take responsibility as the troop commander – to courageously lead your men against the enemy?' Bao Renwen changed his question slightly and tried again.

'Motivation?' Bao Yanrong did not understand.

'What I mean to say, Grandfather, is just why, in fact, were you so brave? Was it because of hatred for the reactionaries, or desire for the liberation of your beloved people . . . ?' Bao Renwen tried to indicate possible answers to his question.

'Oh, motivation.' It seemed that Bao Yanrong had finally understood. 'Wasn't any motivation. Eyes were red with killing, that's all. You'd come down after a battle, if a dog crossed your path, you'd kick him, kick him till he howled. Normally I couldn't kill a chicken – you know me yourself.'

'Oh, well, that's a detail, anyway.' Bao Renwen wrote a few notes in his notebook.

'Son, you're putting so much time into this, let alone the cigarettes . . . What are you really after?' Bao Yanrong was genuinely puzzled.

'I want to write a novel,' Bao Renwen answered.

'A novel?'

'That is, to write a book.'

'Government ask you to write it?'

'No.'

'Commune ask you to write it?'

'No.'

'Then who are you writing it for?'

Faced with this question, which amounted to asking the purpose of literature, Bao Renwen found it hard to give a straight answer himself. It was a question that had been debated by generations of scholars – what could one little aspiring author have to say about it? He said quickly, 'I just want to write, that's all.'

'Can you get any money from a book?' The old revolutionary persisted.

'There's no money in it. During the Cultural Revolution they abolished royalties.' Bao Renwen tried to keep his own patience as he explained.

'Then what do you want?' Again, the question of 'the purpose of literature'.

He did not answer this time, but his smile had a touch of sadness in it. After pausing a moment, he said, 'Grandfather, tell me a little about the Lianxui Campaign.'

Bao Yanrong too was silent for a while, then he reached into his pocket and pulled out his own tobacco pouch.

'Please, take one of these.' Bao Renwen offered him a store-bought cigarette.

'Rather have this, to take away the craving.' Bao Yanrong was determined not to accept any more cigarettes. He felt he had behaved badly before this representative of the younger generation. There was nothing Bao Renwen could do but light the cigarette in his hand and smoke it himself.

The smoke wandered around an oil lamp whose light flickered as it cast their two shadows on the wall, flinging them out so that they writhed like spirits. First tiny, then huge, the shadows on the mouldy wall dominated the entire room. The two of them sat quietly under these shadows, seemingly small and insignificant.

'I want to write a book,' Bao Renwen thought. He had been to the county middle school for two years and learned there about a Soviet writer named Gorky, a man who had never been to school in his life but who had none the less become a great writer. Renwen had a book called *Pioneering* and he heard that the author was also from the countryside. Then there was another book, called *Miles of Forests and Snowy Plains* – the author of that was once an illiterate soldier in the army. These clearly proved that anybody could be a writer – the one thing required, Renwen knew, was diligence. So he hung a sign above his bed at home: 'Diligence Produces Genius'.

He wrote without regard for day or night, wrote on the unused parts of exercise pads from school, wrote until he had several thick books' worth of writing. His parents wanted him to think about finding a wife. He refused. 'Writing first, family second': this too was his secret motto.

People called him Word Crazy: for one, his name meant literature, and for another, he was clearly mad. This nickname was also to distinguish him from someone else. The wife of Bao Chengde was equally loony, but while Renwen's affliction was peaceful, hers was decidedly warlike. When her craziness came on, it took several men to hold her down.

Facing the ridicule of the town, even well-intentioned ridicule, Bao Renwen maintained his composure and kept firmly in mind another phrase – one he wrote at the head of every workbook: 'An eagle can fly lower than a chicken, but a chicken can never fly as high as an eagle.' He kept writing.

CHAPTER 4

In the cowpen, old Bao Bingyi sat on a cot, singing a ballad:

'On Master Guan's door are written these lines,
Teaching us from olden times:
— "One" is like the line of a gun,
二 "Two" is short on top and long underneath,
三 "Three" stood up is like a river,
四 "Four" looks like the walls of a house . . .'

The old revolutionary Bao Yanrong watched him, entranced.

Throughout the singing, the elder son of Bao Yanshan fed the cows, swishing hand-cut hay into the mangers for Bingyi.

Bao Bingyi had joined a travelling opera troupe when he was small, earning the contempt of his family back home. An old man now, he had returned to Baotown: he had left alone, and he came back alone. When asked if he had had a family while he was gone he just shook his head in an almost imperceptible 'no'. Matchmakers tried several times to hitch him up to widows, but he always responded with that small shake of his head.

At one point the rumour went around that he and the lead female star of the troupe had been on intimate terms, but that later she had spurned him. Another story had it that he was interested in the widowed wife of Bao Yanchuan, who lived over to the east. It had been four years since Yanchuan had died, and his widow was burdened with four children – it would be difficult for her to get married again. The trouble was, these people were all of one clan – when you got to figuring out the relationships you would find that the woman should call Bao Bingyi her uncle. These were things that people tried not to think about too much.

Nowadays, as a bachelor, they had him feed the cows. He lived in the cow-pen where he at least had a roof over his head, and the cows had the benefit of someone looking after them.

Although everyone looked down on his former occupation, both old and young loved to hear him sing. They would ask him to perform the old ballads – one stanza could call up five thousand years of history:

一   ' "One" is like the line of a gun.
      Han Xin led his men to fight Ba Wang.
      Ba Wang was pushed back and died beyond Crow River.
      Han Xin died in the Liweiyang Palace.

二   "Two" describes the lines of two dragons.
      Goddess Wang Muniang revealed her power
      When the battle was fought at Flower Bud Mountain
      And the witch was killed at Water Curtain Cave.
三   "Three" is like three parallel streets.
      Chen Shimei begged forgiveness but has not returned.

14

His wife has taken up a lute
And now must beg out on the street . . .'

China's history came wafting out of the cow-pen door.

CHAPTER 5

Dregs was out of control. Crawling now, he managed to get everywhere. His devilish little head was without a single strand of hair, but his smile was wonderful and as his mouth curved up his eyes curved too. People saw him and felt happy. They said he had a natural gift of goodness.

There was little for him to eat, beyond the milk from his mother's breasts. As his father had said, she could make mama from whatever she ate, like an old cow. For a while there were sweet potatoes, but later when these were scarce she made them last by mixing them with leaves.

At New Year his older brother, Construction, turned nineteen,* and still had not found himself a wife. Matchmakers were repelled when they entered the family house – its three rooms were like dark pits; the dirt floors became mud holes when it rained. The family furniture consisted of two wooden beds, whose cotton spreads were so torn they could have been mistaken for fish-nets.

---

* By Chinese custom, everybody is one year older on the seventh day of the lunar New Year.

One day a little urchin came to this household, shaking a bamboo clapper as she begged for food. She was a child of eleven or twelve, with big round eyes. Dregs' elder sister was holding him at the time and standing in the doorway. The little girl planted her feet and stood firm as she shook the clapper rhythmically to accompany her song:

'This older lady
Certainly is fine
Holding her child
Who doesn't even cry . . .'

Dregs' sister, a young woman who had not even left home yet to start her own family, blushed with annoyance as she retreated into the house. Dregs' mother, in contrast, was delighted – she found this little girl oddly pleasing. Ladling some porridge from the pot into a bowl, she handed it to the girl to eat. The child promptly poured it into her own large begging bowl, and announced that she was taking it back for her mother to eat.

'Where is your mother?' asked Dregs' mother.

'Under the big willow tree east of town. She's sick,' the urchin replied, and left.

Dregs' mother could not eat that evening as she mulled this over – it was clear that some idea had taken root inside her head. After dinner she filled another bowl with rice porridge and with this and two pieces of millet flatbread she set off for the east of town.

The old willow tree was the highest point in Baotown. One year, in the summer, when it rained for nine days and nights the entire town was under water except for the twig ends of this tree. They had looked like a clump of grass on a wide prairie, on which had clustered twenty or thirty mice.

There was indeed a sick woman leaning against the base of the tree. The little girl had snuggled up beside her and was engaged in combing out her own braids. She had a wizened face like a little monkey, but the two thick braids were shiny and crow-black. Bao Yanshan's wife went over to join the two of them, and felt the braids with her hand. 'In the old days I had a fine head of hair like that too. I had it braided into one long braid, and I used to tie it with a piece of red string.' She joined thumb and finger in a wide circle to indicate how thick her hair had been.

Before long, Bao Yanshan's wife was seen leading the outsiders towards her home. After two days the face of the older woman was much healthier. When she left Baotown, the young girl stayed behind. Every day this girl would accompany Dregs' second brother, the twelve-year-old Culture, down to The Lake to cut fodder for the pigs. When they returned she would play with Dregs in front of the door, and sing songs for the people attracted by her voice. The young blades of town found her particularly amusing:

'Little Jade, sing us *The Month of December!*'

Hearing this, Bao Yanshan's wife would come storming out of the house, scolding Little Jade and chasing the boys away. 'No singing – what do you think that song is – you're shameless!' She always followed this by a cuff or two. Gradually, Little Jade stopped singing. It was as though her throat had darkened, as though she were mute – she was reluctant even to speak. Whether she sang or not Dregs kept smiling happily at her, until in the end she could not help smiling back.

Everybody liked Dregs. The sole exception was Fifth Grandfather, whose ire was aroused whenever he saw him. The reason was that the moment Dregs hit the earth was precisely when his own son had breathed his last. As a result, Fifth Grandfather was convinced that his son had been taken away and his soul occupied by Dregs.

Fifth Grandfather had been given the 'Five Guarantees'* by

---

* A 'Five-Guaranteed Household': that of a childless and infirm old person who was guaranteed food, clothing, medical care, housing and burial expenses by the People's Commune.

the troop, although the very words made him cringe. To be guaranteed was to be considered a childless person, with no one to take care of you but the troop. This was intolerable to Fifth Grandfather, a stubborn and strong man who would not accept becoming a burden to everybody else. As a result of his unceasing attempts to find a job he was put to twisting new rope out of a mixture of old rope and crushed grass. Every day he sat at the foot of the mill, basking in the sun and twisting rope.

The communal mill enjoyed an unending flow of visitors. Its stone grinding wheel creaked as it ground out grain in the stone basin, turned by a little donkey whose hoofs clapped gently as it walked around. Women clucked to the donkey to step lively as the flour came slowly sifting down from the sieve in to the square bottoms of their bamboo baskets. Listening to all this, Fifth Grandfather felt less lonely.

With Dregs strapped on to her back, Little Jade also came to grind her flour, a basket over one arm, the other leading the donkey. Dregs was placed on the floor as she put the traces on the donkey and the blinkers over its eyes. He sat in the sun picking up stones to play with, right beside the feet of Bao Fifth Grandfather. The old man looked at him with narrowed eyes and softly said one word, 'Devil!'

Hearing it, Dregs quickly put out his small hand, patted Fifth Grandfather on the head, and laughed.

This startled Fifth Grandfather, as he thought how like his own son that laughter was. He felt tears come to his eyes as he added, more gently, 'You devil, you!'

The donkey circled the milling basin as Little Jade clucked softly to him and the flour sifted down.

CHAPTER 6

Bao Bingde's wife had erupted again. She was climbing trees and crawling up in the rafters, and she had already broken all of the breakable pots and pans. Several of the bigger men were dragged for metres as they tried to hang on to her. In the end they got her on her back, with all four limbs pointing skywards, and tied her up. Out of her gnashing teeth and contorted mouth came a yell that was not the sound of a human.

Bao Bingde crouched down with his head in his hands. Bao Yanshan's wife brought him a bowl of sweet-potato porridge so thick you could stand chopsticks up in it, together with two millet flatbreads she had clapped under her arm, but he would not take them – said his insides felt stuffed with worry. There was nothing anybody could do but keep him company.

His wife had been crazy for eight or nine years. Her mother's family had come from the other side of Bao Mountain, and when she was young she was the prettiest thing for miles around. Everybody said Bingde was marrying the peach of paradise. As it turned out, she was good to look at but not for much else: in their first year of marriage she had a miscarriage and bore a dead child. The second year she was pregnant but again it was stillborn – she was pregnant three or four times and every time was the same. Nasty rumours began to be passed around: perhaps as a maiden she had not behaved quite properly? When she bore the fifth dead child she went crazy, and after that people felt too sorry for her to say bad things behind her back.

At the beginning of her craziness there were those who urged Bao Bingde to divorce her and remarry. He refused: 'I can't be so hard-hearted, we were married for life. This is my lot. I can't be hard-hearted.' He did not give any real reasons, just 'I can't be hard-hearted'. Later, Word Crazy wrote a piece for the radio, called *Class Feelings are Deep as the Sea*, or perhaps it was *Class Affections are Vast as the Oceans* – that sort of thing. He sent it to the commune's radio station and it was broadcast. It never made it to the county station, but none the less Renwen's name was already out: it became known that in Baotown there was a person who could 'make words dance'. At the same time Bao Bingde's name got out, and after that piece he could not have divorced his wife if he had wanted to.

As time passed and he tried simply to get along, he began to speak less and less, until he was almost silent. Strangely, he felt a dark hatred for Bao Renwen, as though Renwen had done himself a fine turn but then washed his hands of any responsibility. Bao Renwen in turn felt afraid of Bao Bingde, as though deep down he knew he owed him something. In short, ill feelings arose between the two.

Bao Bingde's wife struggled on the ground, and in no time at all she had clawed out a pit around her. Despite her ferocity, she would never hurt anyone else – except her man, whom she thrashed as though he were a grandson. Bao Bingde was not afraid of her beating: he had her tied up so she would not hurt herself. In the last month of one year* she broke away and ran

---

* The twelfth month of the lunar calendar was the sacrificial month, when sacrifices were offered to the gods and spirits.

down to The Lake, where she jumped into the big ditch that passes through the fields. Forgetting that he could not swim, Bao Bingde jumped right in after her. The two of them had to be rescued and hauled out.

Now, thoroughly depressed, Bao Bingde started to weep. To cover it up he said 'Dammit!' loudly several times, and coughed, and then spat, and got the tears to stop.

'Everything has its end,' said Bao Eryan, trying to comfort him. 'You haven't done anything dishonourable to bring this on yourself. Don't worry so much.'

Dregs' father, Bao Yanshan, was also there. 'There used to be a madman in my mother-in-law's family. When he was crazy he was weird, but before he was crazy he was also weird. Who knows why he went mad – for nineteen years he was like this too, climbing trees. Funny thing was, as soon as his mother died and the coffin was safely in the ground he got better. It was as though he'd had a dream. We all asked him what had happened, and he didn't know a thing about it. It was as though he had been sleeping for twenty years.'

'Is that the truth?' everybody wanted to know, and even Bao Bingde raised his eyes for the answer, as if he saw a thin ray of hope.

'He and his wife have two children by now, fine boys, sane as can be.'

'That's a lot of nonsense.' In the distance squatted Bao Renwen. 'The right thing to do would be to send my seventh aunt to the Municipal Psychiatric Institute.'

'That wouldn't do.' Nobody approved of that course of action.

'So many crazies locked up together – they must rip each other apart.'

'I've heard people say it's just like being sent to jail.'

'The doctors all have clubs with needles in the ends of them.'

'Now that's what I call sick.'

Bao Bingde did not say anything himself, but he stared hatefully at Bao Renwen.

After drawing a long breath, Bao Renwen stood up and walked away. The evening sun made his shadow thin and long. Alone, he set off at an angle into the distance.

CHAPTER 7

Picked-Up and his Aunt slept in separate beds now. When summer came Picked-Up took his cot outside and slept under a tall Chinese scholar tree. When the fall chill set in he brought the cot inside again, and his Aunt was shocked to discover that the room had shrunk and that Picked-Up had grown into a man.

In his solitude, the only one he had been close to was his Aunt. Now he began to distance himself from her as well, in a way which was far worse than for ordinary people. He would not say more than three whole sentences a day: when he ate the only sound was that of food going down. When they finished eating the two of them sat facing each other, without even the sound of eating to keep them company. Full and uncomfortable, there was nothing for them to do but go to bed.

Once in bed, Picked-Up would hear his Aunt's teeth grinding, or her snoring, and he could not sleep. In the daytime, he found that he was always trying to evade her, from a feeling of fear, or of hate – he was not sure which. He knew only that he was frustrated to the point of desperation.

24

Early one morning his Aunt consulted him about selling the pig.

'So sell it.' He spat this out as though there were fire in his belly.

'I was thinking of using the money to buy some cloth, to make you a new bedcover,' his Aunt said.

'So buy it.'

'And to buy you a regular sleeping cot.'

'Go ahead.'

'That summer cot, the Fengs haven't said out loud that they want it, but they're always sounding as though they have a bad need for one.'

'So do it.' It sounded as if he had eaten a number of bullets and was feeling distinctly unwell. His head was down with his face buried in his arms.

'You tell the troop leader you're taking a day off, and see if you can go down to sell the pig.'

'Nope.'

'What do you mean, no?'

'No just means no,' he said stubbornly. He himself did not know why he said no, why he seemed to be irrationally looking for trouble.

'If you won't go, then I will.' She was angry now. These days there was no figuring out this boy.

She changed her clothes, borrowed a flat-bottomed cart, tied up the pig and put him inside. Pushing the cart herself, off she went. A blue skirt was wrapped around her healthy, strong body; her shoulders soon glistened with sweat. Before long she was out on the main road, walking into the rising sun.

Picked-Up squinted his eyes as he watched her. It was not long before he began to regret what he had said. All day he found himself worrying, often lifting his eyes to the sun and then back out to the road. There was a cart coming towards him, but it turned out to be a tall man pushing along a cartload of sweet potatoes.

By the end of the day his Aunt had still not returned.

Picked-Up started the fire for the pot and put on some buns to steam, then he squatted in front of the door to wait. For some reason he began to think of all the good things about his Aunt. That strange fire which had been raging inside him began to melt into a hot warmth which felt more like water pouring through his body. He should behave better towards his Aunt, he thought.

A sliver of moon rose, a thin crescent in a deep blue sky, but bright enough to cover the land with a milky wash.

All of a sudden he began to be frightened. What if something had happened! What time was it? Alarmed, he stood up and set out for town, not taking time to stop and lock the door. Along the road he passed children who had been out cutting grass to feed the pigs. The grass-stuffed baskets on their backs stood higher than a man, making them look like miniature mountains. Picked-Up had always been considered queer by other people, and these children quickly made way for him on the road. His strange face had frightened them all before – how were they to know that their inquisitive eyes made him the one who was scared?

In the moonlight, the whitened road wound up and over the dam, then disappeared.

At the point where it met the horizon, a black insect slowly came into view. It followed the powdery road, getting bigger and bigger. A long, hard look convinced Picked-Up that it was his Aunt.

Striding out, he went as fast as he could to meet her. It was indeed his Aunt, pushing the flat-bottomed cart, and on the cart was a sleeping cot and on top of that a basket. In the basket was fabric, and meat, and also a carton of cigarettes. Picked-Up's eyes got red – had she seen him smoke?

(In shame at not having cigarettes, when Picked-Up smoked, he smoked his homemade pipe with his back to others.)

He charged up, took the handles to the cart, stepped out and soon left his Aunt several metres behind. As he strode along the wheels of the cart creaked, and a cricket piped up from the

26

rustling sorghum to accompany them. The moon covered everything with a transparent radiance. Picked-Up felt a lightness and a clarity inside, which was at the same time calm and joyful. He did not know how things could have changed so completely — to make him feel that life was magnificent, and that living was a gift.

CHAPTER 8

Little Jade was growing up, but her body was slender and the flowered dress from her older sister hung straight to her knees. It was she who laid the fire and cooked dinner, who washed the dishes and cut more fodder than anyone for the pig. People liked her – she had a way about her. The one person she did not pay any attention to was Construction, nor did he ever talk to her.

The two of them could not stand to sit at the same table together. When by chance they ran into each other it was as though both were near-sighted – eyelids would droop and like ancient enemies they would ignore each other. Bao Yanshan's wife felt this was perfectly all right, that this indicated the match was solid and to her solid was good. She was content with everything about Little Jade, except one thing that kept creeping back into her mind: this child was altogether too intelligent.

She often remembered the first time she had seen Little Jade, shaking her bamboo clapper and bravely singing for a meal. Too clever by far, but in fact what she most liked in Little Jade was what she feared. Seeing her son so dumb and mopey, she wondered if the two of them could ever get along. There was not the slightest bit of cunning in Bao Yanshan's wife, and because of this she often wondered if she herself would not in the end be sorry. Whenever she felt her apprehension rising she would order Little Jade about with renewed vigour, as though wanting 'to get the eggs in before the chicken flew the coop'.

'Jade! Feed the pig!'

'Jade, take your brother's clothes down to the river and wash them!'

'Damn lass, I can see the bottom of the water barrel again!'

Little Jade flew about in a sweat until the smile in her eyes gradually went out. As she became serious, her little chin got sharper and sharper, and her two black braids began to show a dull yellow. From time to time people would see her crying under the old willow tree to the east − she would cry noiselessly, then rub her eyes and run towards home again. Those who saw this naturally felt sorry for her, but they also knew that among child-brides★ she was one of the fortunate. She was not beaten and she had enough to eat. If one had to be a child-bride, then Baotown was the place: everybody knew that Baotown folk were kind. It was just a shame they had to be so poor.

With such an assistant helping him cut the grass for the pigs, Culture no longer had to hurry down to The Lake as soon as school was out. He was aware of her merits, and spoke to his 'Jade Sister' as sweetly as possible. When he called to her, Little Jade would blush. Culture not only read books and was not ashamed of being a man of letters, he also had modern democratic ideas about equality between men and women. Watching his mother stridently order Little Jade about he would often stand straight and say, 'I'll fetch the water myself!'

★ A young girl taken into the family as daughter-in-law to be, who also acts as servant until the marriage.

Once, as he slipped the buckets on to his shoulder pole, Little Jade followed along, yelling to him to put them down. Running behind, she pursued him to the well. He snatched at the bucket to lower it into the well, and it came off its hook and fell down into the water. There it floated, deep below the two of them. Culture was stunned.

'Just look at that. What were you in such a rush for, anyway?' Little Jade demanded.

'It was all for you.'

'What are you going to do now?'

'There's nothing hard about this – no problem,' Culture answered, leaning out to try to hook the pail. The rope of the shoulder pole shone in the darkness below.

'Just see if you can!' Little Jade also leaned over, and tried to grab the pole. 'I can get it.' Culture would not let go.

'Give it over.'

'No, I won't.'

The two of them bent over the well. The bucket floated serenely on the water as the hook from the shoulder pole swung back and forth, back and forth. On the water also floated two shadows, one Little Jade, one Culture. The hook from the shoulder pole hooked on to the bucket, but did not pull it up, just stirred it around in the water. After a moment, as the water cleared, the shadows came back again, Little Jade and Culture, as if they were watching a movie.

'See what you look like,' said Little Jade.

'I see that you're awfully pretty, Older Sister,' Culture smiled at Little Jade.

'Oh!' Little Jade spat on him.

'What, is that wrong? You're ugly?'

'That's not the wrong part.'

'What else could be wrong?' Culture was perplexed.

'It's just wrong, all wrong.' Little Jade's former lively self came back as she pointed at him. Culture could not imagine what had happened, and so said nothing more.

The fallen bucket was retrieved and both buckets were filled.

They were hooked on the middle of the pole; Little Jade took the front and Culture took the rear. He put his end of the pole on his shoulder and crouched, waiting for her to start to raise her end. Just as she was ready she stood up again and turned to look at him.

'How old are you, how old am I?'

'You're ox, I'm rat,'* Culture immediately answered.

'Then how can you call me Older Sister?'

He was silent.

'So you see how you were wrong.' She stood up then with the pole on her shoulder, and started smoothly forward while he staggered quickly behind.

The shoulder pole rocked back and forth, the water in the buckets sloshed up and down, up to the edge of the bucket, then down again.

---

* Each year of the Chinese twelve-year cycle is matched with an animal. Someone born in 1951, for example, is rabbit, someone born in 1963 is also rabbit. The order of animals is: rat, ox, tiger, rabbit, dragon, snake, horse, sheep, monkey, rooster, dog, pig.

CHAPTER 9

Dregs could walk now, in a stumbling, erratic fashion, and he could also say a few words. While the family was eating one evening, Bao Fifth Grandfather came shuffling by with his cane. Bao Yanshan called out to him, 'Fifth Grandfather, come have something to eat.'

Dregs picked it up, 'Come eee!'

Fifth Grandfather pretended he had not heard, but he sat down on the stoop and began to watch the ants move house.

'Have you eaten already?' Bao Yanshan persevered.

'Eaten.'

'What did you have?'

'Millet flatbread, porridge and pickled vegetables.'

'Grandpa, if you don't feel like stirring up the fire to cook, come on over here to eat. We've got plenty of people and plenty in the pot – one more or less doesn't matter,' Bao Yanshan's wife said.

'I can cook.' With head hanging low, he stared at the ground. Evening was coming on and soon he could not see the ants anymore. A grasshopper went whirring by.

Something hit his mouth and he looked up in surprise.

32

Dregs had moved over in front of him and his little hands were holding a piece of flatbread. The hands were rolling bits of it into balls and throwing them at his mouth. He looked at Dregs; Dregs looked at him and smiled, full of goodness and honesty. Fifth Grandfather's heart leapt for a moment, then he turned his face away.

The moon rose, cracking open the sky to let in a beam of light.

Bao Fifth Grandfather turned around again; Dregs was sitting at his feet playing with dirt, his scalp showing through a sparse head of yellow hair.* Fifth Grandfather reached out his hand and caressed him while he thought, 'How is it I've seen this devil before?'

In the distance a ballad was coming from the cow-pen, the tune travelling through the night up to the door:

五 '"Five" is the Bottomless Cave Wu Di Dong.
　　 Xiu Rengui crossed the ocean and marched to the east.
　　 Leading his troops and cavalry
　　 He challenged the famous Phoenix City.

六 "Six" opens at the bottom to either side.
　　 I'll take a maiden with skirt and hairpin as my bride.
　　 Leading 3,000 men and horses behind, Xiu Rengui rescued our
　　　　 besieged King of Tang.'

* Because of malnutrition.

CHAPTER 10

In Beijing, a thousand miles away, the battle over the rivers and mountains* was just getting started.

In Shanghai, a thousand miles away, the weapons were ready, and they were preparing to hand out the guns.†

* China.

†The 'Gang of Four' faction (the Shanghai faction of the Central Cultural Revolution Group in China, backed by Mao) started moving against rival political factions which threatened its power in 1976. Mao died on 9 September 1976, and Jiang Qing, Mao's wife, and others in the 'Gang of Four' were arrested in October.

CHAPTER 11

A thrice-new bedcover, new cotton inside, new lining around that and new cover over the lining, wrapped snugly around Picked-Up. He had burrowed himself into its warmth and felt so comfortable that he was not sure he was real. He twisted this way and that to see which comfortable feeling was the very best and as a result did not sleep very well after all.

The moon shone through the brick-hole on to his Aunt's bed nearby: her cotton bedspread was so thin it looked like paper. Picked-Up knew that like paper it was also stiff.

Aunt really loved him, Picked-Up thought. There could never be anyone else who loved him so, not a wife, not a sister, not even a mother. Without any experience of the love of others, Picked-Up was not sure what the love of such people might be like; he only knew that in the whole world the love of his Aunt was best.

It was his Aunt who had spread the bedspread for him, putting one layer under his body, one over, and making sure his feet were tightly tucked in. There was a saying, 'Cold comes in from the soles of the feet.' His feet had not felt so warm in a long time – but this warmth was not the same as that warmth: Picked-Up remembered the soft valley which had warmed his feet in a very special way.

The moonlight moved on to his Aunt's face, which had rounded out these past two years, although wrinkles filled the corners of her eyes. She seemed to shiver and Picked-Up quickly closed his eyes. When he opened them again she had turned to face the wall – the moon now passed softly over her body, its curves, its mounds and hollows.

Several days later Aunt suddenly said to him, 'Picked-Up, you'll be eighteen years old this New Year.'

'Huh,' he answered, a harshness in his voice. Those warm emotions of the night always vanished with daylight, like a receding tide which went somewhere he could not follow.

'And it's time you found a wife.' She paused.

Picked-Up did not say anything now. His heart was pounding.

'Over in Hightown where Ernai's mother comes from there's a girl, just a year older than you – she's fine except for scars left over from the smallpox . . .' She paused again. 'She doesn't care that we're poor – she's willing to spend her life with you. If you want, you could go to Hightown tomorrow for a visit. I had one of the Feng children go to town and get us some fruit for a gift.' She stopped then and did not say anything more. She could hear Picked-Up breathing heavily, like a cow.

The next sound was that of a bowl breaking. Picked-Up had bolted, turning over the cutting board, stool and table, with all its pickled vegetables and fermenting soybeans. Aunt looked at the mess while a chicken wandered in, picked at the smelly soybeans and rejected them.

Picked-Up was gone all day. When he returned the Little Bear was already going down in the west. Aunt had not slept and was sitting on the bed waiting for him.

As soon as he came through the door he went straight to his own bed and jumped inside. He pulled the covers up over his head.

36

'Picked-Up,' his Aunt called to him.

He did not move.

'Picked-Up . . .' She faced the brick-hole and spoke each word slowly and clearly. 'I've brought you a pedlar's pole and rack – Picked-Up, it's time for you to leave.'

He did not move.

'You're grown up now, it's time for you to get along by yourself. I can't raise you your whole life, and you can't take care of me your whole life.'

He did not move, but from his head to his feet he could feel himself turn cold. It was as though he had fallen into a tunnel made of ice.

On a morning when a warm wind was blowing, Picked-Up set out with his pole. Before he left, his Aunt pulled out a pedlar's drum, from who knows where. She gave it a light tap with her hand – tock tock – and the sound was still crisp. She looked at the drum, then at Picked-Up, and opened her mouth – but in the end she did not say anything after all, just quietly handed him the drum.

As he took it, Picked-Up remembered the time he was small, the one and only time he had ever been hit. He had been playing with that very drum and he remembered it well. With feigned indifference he tied it with a string to the back of his pole, then left, never looking back. The drum rocked back and forth from the pole behind his broad back calling out: 'tock tock, tock tock, tock tock'.

Aunt listened until the sound was far away, and then the tears came.

CHAPTER 12

For several days rumours had been going around that a writer would be coming to the county to gather material on flood control.

It was now said that the writer would be coming tomorrow, that his accommodations were arranged and that he would be staying in the county's Number One Guesthouse.

Bao Renwen decided that he had to meet this writer. He spent several days arranging his own pieces of the past year and revising them, and now he neatly copied them out again and stacked them up. Using the shoe sole material that his mother stuck together,* he made a hardback cover by pasting on a shiny sheet from a picture magazine. With brush and ink he wrote 'Collected Works' on the cover, in two strong artistic characters.

Renwen had worked halfway through the night and there

---

* Shoe soles in the countryside are made from layers of paper stuck together with paste. The paste is made by boilir; flour and water; the final product is dried in the sun.

was barely time for a nap before daybreak. He got up, washed his face and brushed his teeth, and then, with his mother's broken comb and some water, carefully slicked down his hair. He put on his blue student's uniform, tucked 'Collected Works' under his arm and set off.

His mother caught up with him after he had gone half a mile, wanting him to take along a basket of eggs to sell on the street. The idea of selling eggs on this important day was revolting – he pretended he had not heard and quickly left town, his legs moving under him like shooting stars.

The sun felt wonderful, warming a cool breeze. It had not rained in half a month and the dust on the road lay ankle-deep. Clouds of it blocked the sun when carts and bicycles went by.

Soon parched, he passed an old farmhouse with a well outside where an old man pulling up water gave him some to drink. He drank half a ladle, then hurried on again.

The empty road stretched into the distance ahead. A tiny black dot appeared way off at the end, and as Renwen watched it gradually grew larger until it took the shape of a person. As he walked on he could distinguish its sex, and finally it took on eyes and eyebrows. The two approached each other, passed, and again the road was empty, drawn into the unseen land before him. The sun was directly overhead now, and Renwen walked along on his own shadow.

He began to feel sleepy, indeed as though he were already asleep. The cover of 'Collected Works' was slippery and kept wanting to slide out from under his arm. He clamped his elbow down securely and walked on.

This bundle was his treasure, it was his heart – to Renwen it was everything there was in the world. How many nights had he stayed up to write it, burning through how many lamps of oil. No matter how tired or sleepy he was, or how hard it was to write a single word, he had forced himself to keep writing, keep writing. At times he wondered why: 'Why suffer? What am I after in the end?' Then a wave of exhaustion would come over him and his mind would go blank. Once when this feeling hit him he actually tore up a piece he had been working on for nine nights.

When that trauma passed he had looked at the torn paper on the floor and wept in desolation. He wanted terribly to lean against someone or something, to warm up a bit, to be comforted. In the end he curled up by himself and slowly calmed down. Then he set out a sheet of paper and took up his pen again. Except for himself there was nobody to lean on, except for writing there was nothing that could help. Only by writing could he keep hold of hope.

The road stretched endlessly before him. It was a lonely, thirsty road, and he did not pass any more wells.

It was afternoon before he got to Liutown; not too far ahead lay the larger county seat. More people met him on the road now, carrying empty shoulder poles after selling their goods in town.

The county seat was quiet. The empty market-place was strewn with chicken bones and fish bones; several women in rags were sweeping out the debris, attracting some dogs. A solitary barber kept his post at the barbershop by leaning back in one of the chairs, snoring. A pig swaggered out of the general store.

Renwen walked past the post office towards the Number One Guesthouse, suddenly beginning to feel a slight alarm. He tried to cheer himself up by thinking of those sentences in 'Collected Works' which had moved him most and given him the greatest satisfaction. But the words that had wrung the very juices from his brain had vanished – he found that he could not remember a single one. He began to realize that the value of the first half of his life, and from this day on the value of the second half of his life, were soon to receive a kind of adjudication. His legs felt shaky and he almost turned back.

The old man in the reception room of the Guesthouse was taking a nap, saliva dripping on to his shirt. A woman behind the desk had her head down, knitting. Nobody paid any attention to him.

He hesitated a moment, then called out, 'Big Sister.'

'Big Sister' frowned and raised her head, looking unfriendly.

'Big Sister, could it be that there is a writer staying here?'

'What writer, how should I know?' she answered.

'I mean somebody who doesn't come from around here, who writes articles, writes books.'

'What's the name?'

'I don't know.'

'Man or woman?'

'I don't know.'

She put her head down and went back to her knitting, not condescending to notice him again.

He tried once more, earnestly calling out 'Big Sister', but there was no longer the flicker of a response. There was nothing to do but find some other way. He stood in the doorway of the Guesthouse, trying to think, then moved off in the direction of the County Party Committee.* A classmate from middle school worked as a typist in the Propaganda Department there – she might be able to help.

With no trouble at all he located the friend, who still remembered him, but when he asked about a writer she knew nothing about it. She suggested asking Division Chief Wang to help.

Division Chief Wang frowned a bit, then clasped his hands together, which involved stretching out his wrists and pushing back his sleeves to expose a shiny new watch. After that he stroked his pomaded, carefully parted hair. 'I'd heard

* The local branch of the Communist Party; that is, the main governing body in the county.

something about this. Yes, but I'm not sure, just not quite sure. I did hear something though.'

'You go and ask Division Chief Zhang for us!' The former schoolmate tugged unceremoniously at her boss's sleeve.

Division Chief Wang turned out to be a lowly worker – the 'Division Chief' was just for appearances. When they finally found Division Chief Zhang the truth emerged. Originally there had indeed been a writer who planned to visit. In the end, though, the writer had changed his mind – perhaps there was insufficient interest in flood control, or perhaps the road to this county was too much trouble. Anyway, the answer was that no writer had come.

Alone again, Bao Renwen walked back down the street, not knowing whether he should feel glad or devastated. He had the distinct impression that he had cast off an enormous stone; he felt light and he also felt very hungry. He had kept a piece of millet flatbread rolled around scallions in his pocket, and he intended to eat this when he got out of town. First he paused to read the newspapers set out in front of the post office.*

In the bottom corner of one was a list of publications – he noticed that it was the catalogue of one of the provincial literary journals. Why not send a manuscript to them? As he thought about it, he felt his face flush with the excitement of a new prospect.

Composing himself, he memorized the address of the journal, then walked into the post office, sat in a corner and began thumbing through 'Collected Works'.

He held the 'Works' below the edge of the table, where no one else could see them, although indeed no one seemed to be watching. In fact there was only one other person in the post office, an old man who looked like a gentleman, wearing a pair of tortoiseshell-framed glasses. He was painstakingly sewing a parcel up in burlap, using a very large

---

* Newspapers are tacked up on long bulletin boards in public places in China.

needle, and a quick glance showed that this was being sent to Qinghai.*

Bao Renwen selected a novel from 'Collected Works', and a piece of prose, and then at the last moment one more novel. He rolled the three together.

The man at the counter demanded, 'What's inside?'

He hesitated, then said, 'Manuscript,' his face reddening.

'What?' The man did not understand.

'Manuscript,' he repeated, his face turning white now. He felt as though he were committing some utterly shameful deed.

The man put the manuscript on the balance, weighed it and then tossed it into a large basket. Keeping his eyes on it, Renwen felt oddly distressed, as if a child he had raised were embarking on faraway travels.

Emerging from the post office, he found that a tranquillity had settled over him. The setting sun was slanting against earthen walls, making the street out of town look golden. The sound of the finger-guessing game rose from the market-place as boys thrust out fingers and fists to the accompaniment of an ancient jingle. A pig snorted contentedly, the loudspeaker was broadcasting a merry tune. He followed his manuscript mentally on its journey and figured out when it might be expected to arrive. From this moment, he could start waiting and anticipating. From now on, he again had a measure of hope.

He felt incredibly lucky. Unconsciously he started humming along with the loudspeaker, then discovered he had the tune wrong and quickly stopped himself. As he walked the sunset hit the clouds behind him. Without seeing them, he was aware of spectacular rays of light.

* A province in the far north-west of China, known for its large labour-camp population.

CHAPTER 13

The sound of a pedlar's drum kept beating in Aunt's ears:
'Tock tock, tock tock, tock tock.'

CHAPTER 14

The sun was already touching the horizon as the rest of the children cutting grass headed home. Little Jade and Culture had come late, and their baskets were still not quite full.

'Culture, you spend so much time there – what do you do in school all day?' Little Jade asked him.

'Go to class, of course. Study Chinese, abacus, geography, history, that sort of thing. Just study.'

'So you call it study! Seems to me you don't know anything, not even how to hook a bucket up out of a well, and you're plain stupid when it comes to cutting pig grass.' Little Jade delighted in teasing him, and only in The Lake did she dare to be naughty.

'Listen, there's plenty that I know and that you don't know.' Culture was not thoroughly convinced of this himself, since he tended to carry a D-average at school. It was only in front of Little Jade that he had a chance to show off.

'Tell me something I don't know, then,' she challenged him.

'Do you know where people come from?' Culture asked.

Little Jade laughed. 'From out of their mothers' stomachs, of course! Is that all they teach you in school?'

With a tolerant smile, Culture asked a deeper question, 'Where do mothers come from? You'll say they come from grandmothers' stomachs, but where do the grandmothers come from? Where do the grandmothers' grandmothers' come from?'

Little Jade was stumped. She flashed her eyes, and could not find anything to say.

'I'll tell you where they come from,' Culture said secretively in a low voice. 'People come from monkeys.'

Little Jade gasped in astonishment.

'If you look at them, monkeys are exactly like men.'

Intimidated, Little Jade whispered, 'Well then, where do monkeys come from?'

Culture hesitated a moment, then said with conviction, 'Monkeys come from fish.'

This puzzled Little Jade – fish and monkeys were not remotely alike. 'Where do fish come from?'

'Now look, you know that on the globe of earth . . .'

'Globe? What's a globe?'

Culture began to feel that this discussion presented unforeseen complications. He could see that rudimentary education of children was an absolute necessity. 'Globe: it means this land we're living on,' he said, stamping his foot. At the same time he stretched out his arms to describe a very large ball. 'On this ball of earth, at the very beginning, the very very very beginning, there was nothing but water – only water.'

'Oh!' Little Jade's head turned in all directions to look in wonder at the darkening sky.

'Water, only water.'

'Just like when it floods,' said Little Jade very softly.

'Does it flood where you come from too?'

'Almost every year. When I was one year old, it flooded like the devil. My mother says the sky was gone, the earth was gone – there was only water.'

'Can you remember?'

'I remember . . . there was a long, long snake.' Little Jade

46

was beginning to feel alarmed. As the sunset deepened, her eyes shone in the twilight.

'Let's go home.' Culture was distinctly frightened.

'When we finish cutting, then we'll go home.' She dropped down and cut a clump of grass.

He bent down too and cut a clump of weeds. 'Let's go home!'

'Nobody's going to blame you if your basket's not full, but if I come home half empty, that's another story.' She was suddenly upset.

'Are you trying to say that my mother isn't fair?' Culture found that hard to accept.

'Fair? There's no mother more unfair than your mother in the whole world!'

'How can you say nonsense like that?' Culture also began to get angry.

'What nonsense? Why does your mother let you go to school and not your older brother?' Little Jade turned a pair of penetrating eyes on him.

After a few seconds, he stammered, 'My brother is a good, honest person.'

'Who says he isn't honest?' She lifted up her basket, stepped over two clumps of sweet-potato tops and kneeled down again.

'Honest people are dependable.' Culture felt he should be loyal to his less clever older brother.

Little Jade was cutting pig grass as fast as she could. No blade was going to escape those sharp eyes, and her hands were as fast as her eyes. After a while she said, 'Culture, from now on how about telling me what you've learnt in school?'

'Sure, that's OK,' he said, then changed his mind. 'Well no, maybe not.'

'I'll make it worth your while – I'll sing songs for you.'

'Sing *The Month of December*,' he said immediately. He had heard about this song from the older boys in town, but he did not know what it was really about. He was itching to find out.

47

Little Jade paused a moment, and then sang:

> 'First month starts the New Year – Laugh and smile, everything
>   is new.
> Just hard to find a lover
> Who I can pour my heart out to . . .'

She sang with feeling, not understanding a word. She had heard adults sing the song and had joined in and got to know it, then discovered that its poignancy suited her mood.

She sang, lonesome, and Culture listened, also lonesome.

CHAPTER 15

Dregs was successful in getting Fifth Grandfather to accept his flatbread. The stubborn old man still refused any food sent by others, as though accepting it would immediately brand him a real end-of-the-liner. When Dregs brought food, though, he found he had trouble saying no. The sight of that little face made him feel that not taking it would be wrong.

Dregs could chatter like nobody else, and he knew that pestering Fifth Grandfather with questions would often take the edge off his loneliness.

'Have you eaten yet?' he asked Fifth Grandfather.

'Yep, eaten; you?' Fifth Grandfather paid his respects.

'Ate a while ago.'

'What did you have to eat?' Fifth Grandfather asked.

'Some noodles.'

'Not bad.'

'What did you have?' Dregs asked Fifth Grandfather.

'Millet flatbread, rice porridge and fermented soybeans.' Each word was spoken clearly, without the slightest ambiguity.

'Cricket,' said Dregs, holding it up for Fifth Grandfather to see.

'Yes, it's a cricket,' Fifth Grandfather nodded.

'Is it a man or a woman?'

Fifth Grandfather laughed. 'You rascal, with crickets you don't say man or woman, you say male or female.'

'Is it male or female?'

Fifth Grandfather pondered a moment, then said, 'Come to think of it, saying man or woman's just as good – that's gender too.'

Dregs suddenly raised his head and said, 'Let's let him go!'

'Fine – let him go.'

An old man and a young child stood together watching a cricket – in one quick jump it disappeared.

Dregs and the second little boy in the Bao Renyuan family used to play 'Beat the General' together. Fifth Grandfather helped Dregs prepare his generals: when the poplar leaves were falling they would gather them up and carefully cut the leafy part away from the centre stem, keeping the stem for drying. Each would use a shoe to keep his stems, a big one for Fifth Grandfather and a small one for Dregs. After drying, the stems would be good and tough – tougher than hemp, and certainly tougher than the tender stems that little Second Son used. The game was to pull these stems, one boy on each end, and see whose generals were tougher: Dregs won, Second Son lost, Dregs won, Second Son lost. Second Son's eyes began to be teary, and the more teary they got the more his tender stems broke. Finally Dregs took all of his own generals and gave them to Second Son.

Then the order of battle changed: Dregs lost, Second Son won, until in the end Dregs lost terribly. Instead of getting upset, he was his usual cheerful self. Fifth Grandfather watched all this from the sidelines, and when Second Son had gone he asked, 'Dregs, why did you take all your generals and exchange them for Second Son's?'

'Because I could see he was about to start crying.'

'Doesn't it bother you to lose?'

'Yes, it does bother me.'

'And you still gave them to him?'

'I could see he was about to start crying,' Dregs said once again.

Fifth Grandfather did not say any more. He looked at Dregs, gave the thin hair on his head a rub, and sighed. After a while, he said as though to himself, 'And in fact you did the right thing, for when you think about it, he's your uncle.'

CHAPTER 16

Aunt kept hearing the beat of a pedlar's drum: 'Tock tock, tock tock, tock tock.'

CHAPTER 17

Every day after work now Bao Renwen walked east of town
to see if the postman was coming. The day before last the
postman actually did come, and he carried two letters: one
from Bao Shanhai's oldest boy, now in the army, the other
from the family of Bao Erye's wife. This wife had been brought
to Baotown from the far north-east, beyond the eastern pass*
the year Bao Erye went there as a homesteader. Yesterday the
postman also came by, but he was not carrying any letters for
Baotown – just passing through on his way to the town of
Daliu.

Today when Renwen went out on the main road he heard
in the distance what sounded like a pedlar's drum: 'Tock tock,
tock tock, tock tock'. Before long he saw a man coming
slowly towards him, balancing his goods on either side of his
pole.

---

* Shan Hai Guan, the pass at the north-eastern end of the Great Wall, marking the
boundary of China's eastern frontier. Braving the grim life beyond the pass was a
final option, done only when a livelihood could no longer be made in China proper.

Behind the pedlar was a blood-red sun, which seemed to have stopped just as it touched the end of the road. The pedlar walked along, his drum going, 'tock tock, tock tock, tock tock'.

'Brother,' Renwen asked in a loud voice, 'have you seen anyone in a cart coming down this road?'

'No, I haven't,' the pedlar replied, as he approached. His head was shaved so that the skin shone white against the dark tan of his face and neck. His shoulders were broad and strong, although the soft hairs on his upper lip were still curly.

'Older brother, what's the name of that town up there?'

'Baotown,' Renwen said as he turned in disappointment to go back home.

'So this is Baotown,' the young pedlar said. He joined Renwen and together they walked towards town.

'You mean you know Baotown?'

'Of course I do. This place has quite a reputation – people are kind here, everybody knows that.'

'Oh.' Renwen did not ask further.

Looking around as they entered town, the pedlar soon attracted a group of housewives. They heard the drum and came poking their heads out of doors.

'Brother, stop just a minute, I'd like to buy a thimble,' called one. She looked around forty. Tufts of hair stuck out over her ears, escaped from an unruly bun. Her dress was so ragged it seemed to be two pieces of old cloth hung front and back. A strong, firm body showed through these as she moved. She stepped up to his case of goods and pulled a thimble from one of the boxes. Her wrists were round, the eyelashes on her downcast eyes were long.

'Finished work, Big Wen?' She said hallo to Renwen.

'Hallo, Second Aunt, are you buying a needle?' He said hallo back to the widowed wife of Bao Yanchuan.

Several more ladies arrived, wanting needles and spools of thread. Bao Yanchuan's widow had trouble selecting just the right thimble and she was taking her time about it. 'Second

Aunt, you won't be able to tell one from another before long,' Bao Yanshan's wife complained to her.

'So I'm only buying a thimble – I still want the very one that suits me,' she answered, and patiently kept on trying every single one.

'Older brother, where have you come from?' Bao Yanshan's wife asked the pedlar.

'From over on the other side of the mountain.'

'Do you have parents over there?'

'No.' He said it in a muffled voice.

'Have any brothers or sisters?'

'No.'

'You've had a rough life, child, I can see that.' She could not help feeling sorry for him, looking at his big eyes and honest manner.

Bao Yanchuan's widow was still trying on thimbles, as though she were selecting a ring. Now she too turned around to look at him. 'What's your name?'

'Picked-Up,' he said. He noticed that this woman's voice was pleasantly low and resonant. Listening to it was like having a basin of warm water poured over your body.

Finally she made her choice, and took a two-fen* bill from her pocket. As he received it it was still warm and slightly damp.

A crowd of wives now surrounded him, looking him up and down until he began to sweat. 'Well, well!' They all clucked in sympathy at his hard life.

Awkward as the situation was, he soon found himself soaking up the warmth of their attention. For the first time since leaving Fengtown,† he found that he was smiling.

Unperturbed by all the hands reaching into his cases, pawing

---

* Two fen is roughly half a cent at 1988 exchange rates.
† Literally 'Feng Well', since a well indicated a town. In Beijing, a number of the streets also used to be called such-and-such well.

over the various things he had to sell, he happily sat down and began to take out his pack of cigarettes. No sooner had he discovered that there were none left than he felt something warm being put into his hands – a tobacco pouch. Raising his head, he saw the woman who had bought the thimble looking straight at him. 'Have a smoke!' she said, then turned and left. Her rags swished around her body as she climbed the earthen bank to her house and went inside.

That night, Picked Up slept together with the ballad-singer in the cow-shed. In the evening the room was, as usual, full of people gathered to hear Bao Bingyi sing.

七   ' "Seven" has its leg kicked out to the side.
        Master Guan carries a long knife curved like the moon.
        Master Guan, where are you going?
        Off to catch Cao Cao on Ba Wang Bridge.

八   "Eight" has two sides propped up on each other.
        Eight immortals pass through the Eastern Sea.
        Lan Cai He plays with two moon plates.
        The Dragon King of the Four Seas is in trouble.'

CHAPTER 18

Bao Yanshan's wife was perplexed. Little Jade had been running around under her nose every day: how, without her noticing, had she managed to grow up so fast? The body which had been straight as a section of bamboo now was rounded – round breasts, curvy legs – even her little chin was less pointed.

People began to say to Bao Yanshan's wife, 'You have to get that child married.'*

She talked it over with her husband. 'Time to get Little Jade married.'

Construction was already twenty-four: time to get them married.

Little Jade soon felt a subtle change around her. Her stepmother was unusually good to her, not even yelling when she broke a bowl, just telling her to go and sweep up the pieces and to mind that Dregs did not cut his feet. That was all.

---

* Literally, 'to give her a round chamber', the 'round' meaning lucky, auspicious, complete. 'Matters of the chamber' are matters of sex.

Culture, on the other hand, stopped joking with her and began to keep his distance. As for Construction, he spent his time fixing up the inner room, filling in the deeper holes of the dirt floor, painting fresh whitewash all over the walls. The women in town began to look at her sideways as they put their noses together, devious and secretive as they could be.

Little Jade pulled Dregs out of the room one day and hauled him to the well, to have a talk.

'Dregs, does your sister Jade treat you well?'

'She treats me better than my own sister,' Dregs said truthfully.

'Then why do you trick your sister Jade?'

'I don't.'

'You do,' Little Jade accused him.

'But I don't, I don't!' Dregs was getting agitated.

'OK, you don't trick me. Now tell me, what have mother and father been saying about me these past few days? What's going on at home?'

'My older brother is going to take a wife,' Dregs said.

Little Jade felt as though something had exploded inside her head. She calmed herself and praised Dregs, saying, 'You're a good boy, Dregs, telling the truth. You go along home now.'

'Where are you going to go, then?' Dregs wanted to know.

'I'll stand here a while,' she said, then changed her mind. 'Actually, I'm going to go to Second Aunt's house to borrow a shoe sole pattern.'

Dregs left, but after a short distance hid himself behind a tree to watch. The child had a keen eye.

Little Jade walked aimlessly in a circle for a moment, then very slowly started walking towards the east. Soon she was walking faster and faster, until Dregs could not keep up behind.

She ran to the foot of the old willow tree, fell down and hugged it, and then began to cry, sobbing over and over again, 'I'm only sixteen!'

Dregs had immediately gone home to report the news, and

soon Bao Yanshan and his wife came running, together with most of the rest of the town. They tried to get Little Jade to go back home but she clung desperately to the tree, and as she clung she kept calling, 'I'm only sixteen! I'm only sixteen!'

Those standing around could not help beginning to sympathize, and some even began to cry – particularly those who had recently left home as young brides themselves. This last group was soon dissolved in tears.

Bao Yanshan's wife, crying herself, begged Little Jade to talk to her. 'The two of us have been together for so many years – what is it you can't say to me, that you have to take it out like this?'

Little Jade only beat her head on the tree as the tears flowed out with the words, 'I'm only sixteen! I'm only sixteen!'

'Your mother, your father, we haven't deceived you, we only want you to marry – Construction will be twenty-five at New Year . . .' Bao Yanshan's wife was crying even harder than Little Jade now. Hurt and aggrieved herself, the tears were like a small brook running down her cheeks.

'I'm only sixteen! I'm only sixteen!'

'I know that Construction was born pretty stupid, but he has a good heart, child, you won't be hard up with him.'

'I'm only sixteen!'

'You'll be the oldest, the number-one wife in the family. This household will belong to you. Child, think about your mother too.'

Little Jade shook her head and refused to answer. She firmly clutched the tree and could not be dragged away. Not until Bao Yanshan faced the assembled audience and announced that the marriage would be postponed for two years did her arms finally relax.

The incident passed. Little Jade's chin once more grew sharp and pointed, although the rounder parts of her body did not go back to being flat. Her eyes were more serious now, and she seldom showed even the silk thread of a smile. Her stepmother grew stingy with her again, while Culture went out of his way to be more kind. If he saw her sweeping he would take the broom from her and sweep himself. Little Jade, on the contrary, had taken a dislike to him — she would throw the broom down on the ground and march away.

Finally came the day when Culture intercepted her at the well, and asked, 'What is it, Little Jade? What have I done to you?'

'You haven't done anything to me.'

'Then why are you so upset?'

'Upset because you haven't done anything,' she said coldly. Then she shouldered the pole and was about to lift the water and leave.

Culture held down the pole and would not let her lift it. 'What do you mean? Speak clearly.'

'My words couldn't be more clear.'

'How is it I still don't understand?'

'You've got no ears, and you've also got no heart.'

'What are you blaming me for?'

'Just blaming you, you gutless bum!' With that she pulled up with all her might, catching Culture off-balance. He fell flat on his rump, startled and mad.

Little Jade began to laugh, a clean, clear laugh that startled the birds out of trees around. Since the incident, it was the first time she had laughed.

Hearing it, Culture could not be angry.

CHAPTER 19

Bao Bingde awoke early one morning to hear his wife say, clearly and distinctly, 'I haven't made things easy for you either.'

He felt his chest tighten and a lump come to his throat. His wife was already crying. 'I've been a burden on you for half a lifetime. It's time it came to an end.'

That line of thought did not sound promising, and he quickly tried to deflect it. 'What do you mean, an end? When we married, we married for life – for better or for worse, our lives will be spent together.'

Without answering, she wiped her tears and went out to feed the pig. She cooked the feed until it was good and thick, stirring it smooth. Her gleaming hair was combed smooth and tied into a neat bun; she had put on a deep blue skirt that fitted, which made Bao Bingde stare in amazement.

He remembered how she had been as a young girl, when he carried two bags of fruit over to take a look at his prospective in-laws. He had walked through the gate and seen a young woman sitting at the door, embroidering soles.* She looked at

* Given as dowry.

him, he looked at her: the full, round moon of her face was fringed with long bangs. They accented finely curved eyebrows and smiling upturned eyes. He was hypnotized; she blushed and retreated into the ramshackle house, leaving the image of a single long braid swinging back and forth.

He remembered how she had been at the wedding ceremony, that single braid tied into a mountainous bun behind her head. In the glossy black hair was a crimson ribbon. She wore a short red jacket, and her face was like a peach blossom. She sat erect, oblivious to the exclamations of the guests. Bao Bingde had wished the guests would leave and let them be alone.

He remembered how she had been when she was first pregnant. In those days if she wanted something sour he would not think twice about going to the other side of the mountain to find unripe apricots for her. Every night he would kneel down beside her to listen to her stomach, but what he heard was the lonely sound of one heart beating.

He remembered that he had had a dream then of her giving birth, and what came out was a large egg which turned into a sweet potato. When she gave birth to a dead child he closed the door and beat her. Without a sound or a protest she let him pound her and kick her, and afterwards willingly did whatever she was told. She had not minded the beating, but later he was miserable, regretting what at the time he had been helpless to stop. Nobody on the outside knew that anything had happened.

In time, her lovely round face became haggard, her colour faded. A day came when Bao Bingde returned home from work and found the room unswept, the fire cold and the dishes all broken. He was on the verge of getting angry when he saw his wife sitting on a small stool, pulling out her own hair, and at the same time sweetly smiling at him . . .

'Time to go to work!' She brought him out of his reverie. At that, he finally heard the gong beating, announcing the start of the work-day. He rubbed his eyes, stood up and left.

In The Lake, working in tandem with Bao Erye, he announced, 'Looks like she's cured! This morning she was rational when she talked to me.'

'What did she say?' Bao Erye asked.

Bao Bingde repeated precisely what had been said. Unexpectedly, Bao Erye turned pale as he threw down his shovel. 'That's bad news, Bingde.'

'What?' Bao Bingde felt the hair on the back of his neck rising. He had known all along that something was not right, but could not say exactly what it was.

'Number Seven, you'd better go right home and look after her,' Bao Erye urged.

'But this morning she was clear as a bell, much better than I've seen her in ages.' The more he protested, the more he began to feel alarmed.

'It's that clearness that's wrong – when she's muddled she's fine.' Bao Erye stamped his feet in emphasis.

Several men had gathered around to listen, and now they took turns encouraging Bao Bingde to go home and look after his wife. Sweat was pouring down his forehead as he picked up his shovel and left.

With long hard strides he headed home, across levelled land that stretched as far as he could see. In the distance stood one green tree, marking Baotown. He seemed to walk for miles without getting nearer to it. All around him was stillness; the men's voices carried faintly from over the fields. The sun was high, scorching his back. A bird called. A soft breeze hugged the ground, brushing grasses against his legs.

As he approached, the town was quiet and empty. A child carrying water appeared to slip by the poplar windbreak, but when he looked more closely the child had disappeared. He had been walking so fast that he was panting, and now he slowed down. It was all a false alarm, he told himself, just look at how peaceful this place is. Several chickens came by, pecking at the earth; a dog lounged out of an alley, greeting him with a lazy growl. The sun shone down brightly.

He let out a sigh of relief, and laughed at himself for being so susceptible to worry. It had not been worth it to come all this way back from The Lake. He shouldered his shovel and slowly climbed the embankment to his house.

One lone chimney in the village had smoke coming from it, but this was somebody else's house.

The door was closed. It did not budge when he pushed: it had been bolted from the inside. He began to knock, calling, 'Hey!' as he did so. He called her 'Hey', and she also called him 'Hey'. They could not, as others did, call each other Mother and Father: they had no children and as a result they lacked even a proper name.

No sound came from inside.

He called again, 'Hey!'

Still no response.

Afraid now, he began beating on the door. Soon he started kicking it, and then he pounded with his shovel until its head came off. A group of small children and older women, attracted by the noise, joined in calling and knocking until at last the door was forced open. Bao Bingde collapsed on the floor as he saw before him a deep blue skirt, swaying over a stool that had been kicked over. His wife had hung herself from a beam.

The crowd rushed in to take her down. She was still alive: she had failed to put the rope in the right place. With a sob, Bao Bingde put his arms around her and held her, and the room was suddenly full of people wailing.

Dregs had gone to The Lake to call back the working men and in a short time a group of them, breathing heavily, had assembled at the house. Bao Renwen pulled Bao Bingde away from her body and started blowing into her mouth. He had learned artificial respiration in middle school one year. The troop leader organized the preparation of a makeshift stretcher; she was put on it and carried away.

'Money!' Bao Bingde called hopelessly after them, 'I have no money for the hospital!'

'The troop will get some together for you,' the troop leader called back.

'Everybody will get it together for you,' the crowd yelled to him, and with that he came stumbling along behind them.

Two days later, Bao Bingde pushed his wife back home in a flat-bottomed cart. She sat on the boards, gnawing at a green peach like a three-year-old child. She remembered nothing: it was as if nothing at all had happened.

CHAPTER 20

The village schoolmaster was urging Dregs to go to school. Dregs was seven now: time to learn to read and write.

The problem was that Culture was already in the commune middle school, and the family could not find tuition for two children. As the father of the family said, it was either Dregs or Culture.

Two years ago, this could easily have been resolved – then Culture was only too anxious to quit. Lately, though, he seemed to have found the key, and all of a sudden learning was a pleasure to him. From being the last in class he moved up to first. Baotown boasted only three children who had passed the exam to enter the commune middle school – Culture had been first among them. He put a lot into studying now, and it was not easy. School was a good six miles from home: the family had not been given food coupons for the cafeteria, so his daily lunch consisted of one rolled piece of flatbread softened with a cup of tea.

Dregs also wanted to go to school. All the schoolchildren in town had red scarves around their necks, and these aroused his envy and admiration. He did not know what they meant but he knew what they did: they made children good.* One day Second Son's scarf was taken back by the teacher because he had been fighting and had knocked out somebody's tooth. Clearly, a scarf did not come from doing bad things, it only came from doing good.

His father said that it would be best to have Dregs go to school – Culture could write already and was able to do his sums. That was enough, and besides, having him at home to work would be a great help. Culture would not have it: he cried, he yelled, he would not eat, until finally Dregs said, 'Let him study, I'll stay home.'

So Culture stopped crying and went down to The Lake to catch Dregs a cricket. Little Jade wove sorghum stalks together to make him a cage. Dregs played with it a while, then let it go, saying, 'It's too sad, alone in a cage like that.' His father promised to send him to school next year.

Dregs continued to spend his days cutting pig grass with the smaller children. They stayed close to him, liking to be in his presence. If one walked too slowly, Dregs would wait for him, if one cut too little grass and was afraid to go home, Dregs would split his own half and half. If someone started to fight, Dregs would not let it continue. Parents felt at ease when they knew their children were with Dregs. 'A good boy,' everybody said.

Although Dregs could work now, Bao Fifth Grandfather could not – he had ceased to be able even to make rope. All he could do was sit by a wall taking in the sun. He would sit until noon and then slowly get up to go home to cook. Dregs would not allow that. 'Come to our house to eat!'

Bao Fifth Grandfather would not refuse. After some time of this, Dregs' father said to him, 'You're always asking Fifth Grandfather over here to eat – what if we don't have enough for ourselves?'

---

* The red bandannas were worn by Young Pioneers, the model children of China's Communist Party.

Very conscientiously, Dregs answered, 'I'll eat one less flat-bread and one less bowl of porridge.'

His father smiled, and rubbed his son's head.

That day, the older sister who had been married out to the other side of the mountain came home, bringing her child with her. Without a bed, Dregs went to spend the night with Fifth Grandfather. They lay side by side, Dregs' little body held close by the other, like a cat. 'You make my bed all warm, Dregs,' Fifth Grandfather told him.

'I'll warm your bed for you every night, Grandfather,' replied Dregs.

As they snuggled together, Fifth Grandfather felt a rare peace. He became more talkative than usual.

'Dregs, did your father say you could come sleep with Fifth Grandfather?'

'My dad trusts me,' Dregs said.

'Did your mother give permission?'

'My mother trusts me too.'

'They'll say that this old man is a great big nuisance.'

'No, they won't.'

'I just won't kick the bucket, you see, even though I'm so tired of living.'

'The best days are yet to come,' Dregs said earnestly. 'Second Son goes to school every day, and he says that the teacher tells them, "the best days are yet to come". He says the Gang of Four has been put down and in no time flat we'll see better days.'

'Dregs, do you want to go to school?'

'I do.' Then, immediately after, 'No, I don't.'

Fifth Grandfather could tell he wanted to. 'How much is the tuition?'

'A lot, more than three yuan.'*

'Then Fifth Grandfather will pay it for you.'

* Roughly US 8oc at 1988 exchange rates.

'You can't, Fifth Grandfather, your money comes from the central pot . . .'

This reminded him. 'You're right, I'm eating other people's food, I'm an end-of-the-liner.'

'Fifth Grandfather, how can that be true when we all call you Gramps!'

'You little devil! You certainly know how to talk.' After a moment, he murmured, 'You're a little like my own son, Society.' But Dregs did not hear this since he had already fallen asleep. 'Just like him in the eyes, and also the disposition.'

Dregs slept quietly. Not even a whisper of breath came in and out his nose. The brick-hole had been stopped up and the room was so dark you could not have counted your fingers.

'Just like Society, kind and good. Never arguing with people,' Fifth Grandfather said to himself in the dark.

A small cricket at the foot of the wall called back in answer.

CHAPTER 21

The sound of a ballad issued from the cow-pen:

九 ' "Nine" hangs a golden hook on itself.
Seven wolves and eight tigers
Are exiled to a lonely land.
Count up ten to make it complete,
Liu Bang left and never came back . . .'

CHAPTER 22

Picked-Up walked on for two days, then turned around. He tucked his pedlar's drum into his pants so that it would not knock and walked back to the place where he had first put down his pole to sell goods. He yelled up to the nearby house, 'Second Aunt!' Hearing her name, she emerged, wearing a skirt which was not, this time, revealing. Her hands were covered with the dough of yellow sorghum flatbread.

'Brother, why have you come back?'

'When I was here before I walked off with your tobacco pouch – I've come to return it.' He pulled the pouch from his pocket and held it out, facing her.

'Was that worth coming all the way back for? Take it – I'll give it to you, I don't want it.' Her voice was low and rough, with an edge of sweetness in it – it was enough to put a man thoroughly at ease.

'No, I couldn't do that.' Picked-Up advanced to her stoop as he said this, holding the tobacco pouch out in front of himself.

'I can't take it,' Second Aunt said, stepping backwards as she held out hands that were covered with flour.

'I can't keep it,' said Picked-Up, as he began to climb the stairs.

'Well then, here, put it in my pocket for me!' She held a hip out, indicating the place on her skirt.

Picked-Up put his hand inside her deep warm pocket. It lingered a moment before coming out again, keeping with it a little of her warmth.

'Come in and sit a minute, have a cup of tea,' she said.

'No, I'll be going.' As he said this, his feet did not move an inch.

'Sit and rest a moment,' she repeated.

'I'm going,' he said again, but he did not go.

'Come in and sit down, for heaven's sake!' she insisted now, and nudged him with her shoulder. He promptly walked into the house.

With three rooms, the house was not small, but it was absolutely bare. Two children were crawling on the floor, one around three years old, the other around four. A flat griddle was set up on bricks by the door. While Second Aunt continued to knead the dough, Picked-Up sat on a bench and smoked.

'Which children are these?' he asked.

'Number three and number four,' she said.

'Adorable children.'

'They're pests.'

Sentence by sentence, they began chatting with each other. He did not know why, but he felt self-assured and comfortable with her. On this second meeting, he felt he had already known her for a long time.

'Their father hasn't come back from work yet?' he asked.

'Gone to be a ghost, not to work – he's dead!'

'Oh.' Finally, he said slowly, 'You must have had a hard time of it.'

'I'm used to hardship. Brother, could you help me make a fire under that griddle?'

He stood up quickly and got to work.

'Brother,' she called to him again.

'Yes?'

'You've come from over on the other side of the mountain – have they divided the land up over there too?'

'Looks like it's going to happen soon – they're making a lot of noise about it.'

'When the land's divided, then this family will really have something to worry about.' She drew a long breath.

'Surely everyone will help out – the people in this town are known for their generosity.'

'Listen, as soon as they split up the land, work becomes food – it becomes money. Who knows what's going to happen then?'

'With everybody in Baotown having the same last name, surely so long as anybody has food they won't begrudge you some.'

'Brother, you sure are good at talking,' she laughed.

'I may be stupid, but what I'm saying is true,' Picked-Up blushed.

'Yes, what you're saying is true,' she glanced at him, saying it softly as though persuading herself it was so.

The dough was ready. Second Aunt moved her stool to sit in front of the griddle. Reaching over it, she placed a large round of rolled-out dough on to the hot surface. A cloud of steam sizzled up and Picked-Up felt his spirits rise with it – he seemed to see his own Aunt's face in that steam.

A bamboo spatula quickly turned over the flatbread, and as the steam cleared, the face again was that of Second Aunt. 'Stay and have something to eat,' she said.

'Better not,' he mumbled. Without paying attention to him, she put another flatbread on the griddle, a shiny round, then in a moment turned that over too. He watched her hands as she worked: round wrists, chubby fingers. The skin on the backs of her hands was slightly wrinkled, but still firm. He had seen many hands already, as ladies reached out for his goods – so many pairs of them had turned this way and that, deliberating over a purchase. Never had he seen a pair that made him feel the way these did: the first sight of them gave you, how to say it, a feeling of intimacy, of warmth. It was as though he had seen those hands somewhere before – otherwise how could they have been so familiar?

'You also have a rough life,' Second Aunt said quietly. 'When you're out on the road stop by here sometimes and take a rest, have a cup of tea, have a meal – consider this home a place to put your feet up.'

Picked-Up felt his throat tighten, and he could not answer.

'If you have anything that needs washing, just leave it here. Going around like that by yourself – it isn't easy.'

'Second Aunt!' Picked-Up's voice was full of emotion as he said her name.

CHAPTER 23

For once, there was no sound of a pedlar's drum beating in Aunt's ear. She slept soundly throughout the night.

CHAPTER 24

The land was redistributed. Now, no matter how much Culture pleaded, he was not going to go to school – he was needed at home to work their new land. As a final recourse, he went to Bao Renwen, who had a word with Bao Yanshan.

'Uncle, you need to be a little more farsighted. Now they've split up the land, we'll all be wanting to grow more to sell. What we harvest will depend on our own resources, our own abilities. Best is to let Culture go to school, learn the scientific way to farm – depending on muscle alone for crops just isn't the way.'

Bao Yanshan kept smoking without saying a word.

Bao Renwen then opened the newspaper he had brought, and began to read aloud: in such and such a place a student had made himself rich by raising angora rabbits; in such and such a place another student had planted his rice scientifically and also made a lot of money. Bao Yanshan's eyes began to open wide, listening to these successes, but when the conversation came around again to Culture he went back to his mute rejection. It was as though Culture and those success stories had no connection at all. He let Bao Renwen have his say, but was not moved at all by his argument. His answer was, 'Far-away water can't put out a nearby fire.'

'It's still better to get some education!' Bao Renwen was getting combative, and by this time Culture was sobbing uncontrollably.

Bao Yanshan narrowed his eyes and simply looked at Renwen, who was, in fact, a most inappropriate person to do this particular job. He was a persuasive argument against his own position, living proof that education only leads to trouble. People had only to look at him to be reminded of the perils of schooling: it was clearly a waste of time and money to fill a child with words.

After that it was pointless to keep on trying. Culture knew he might as well save his energy for work and he stopped crying. Little Jade, on the other hand, had something to say about the matter when they were alone: 'So you're giving up, are you?'

'Can't help it, it's hopeless.' Defeated, he hung his head.

'Cur!' Little Jade scornfully spat out the word.

Culture's face went red. In Baotown, the worst thing one could be called was 'cur'. It had all the connotations of being cowardly, stupid, shiftless, a bastard and an idiot. One could not have self-respect and at the same time be a 'cur'. Culture's lips moved but he was too shocked to speak as he stood up to leave. Little Jade darted towards him and grabbed him by the arm.

'You give me back those songs I sang for you!'

'. . . How can I do that?'

'Sing them to me! Sing *December*!' she demanded.

'I can't sing.'

'It doesn't matter if you can or not: just sing.'

He stood dazed, knowing he was no match for her, and also no match against the demon in his heart that felt so warmly towards her. 'Well . . . can I sing a different song?'

'That would do.' Little Jade was accommodating.

Culture thought for a moment, then said, 'I'll sing a revolutionary song.'

'Sing!'

He hummed to himself briefly, cleared his throat, and then launched into the song. 'Heavy waves on the wide, wide river . . .' He paused to sneak a look at her and see her reaction. He was afraid she would laugh.

She was not laughing, but looking at him with her mouth slightly open, as though surprised.

'The wind blows the budding rice, making both sides of the river fragrant. My home is there on the bank of the river . . .' He glanced sideways as he sang, and saw that she had grown pensive.

'I'm used to the whistle of the boatman . . .' Culture sang until his throat was sore and he thought it best to admit defeat. 'I really can't go on.'

As if waking up, Little Jade raised her eyes to look at him, and said softly, 'That certainly is a pretty song.'

Relieved and proud, Culture felt he had wiped out the humiliation.

As news of his not going to school got around, the village schoolmaster came to the house to try to pry loose Dregs. In a final effort, he resorted to the ultimate tactic of asking for face.

'To tell you the truth, I've been a schoolmaster for all these years, but I have yet to be put on the State payroll.* If you'd let Dregs go to school it would give me face — I'll pay the tuition for his first semester myself!'

Bao Yanshan looked at this man, and finally he nodded his head. He would not let him pay the tuition, though. He said, 'If I really let him go to school then I'll be the one who pays — I couldn't let you reach into your own pocket for it.'

He was as good as his word. Not only did he pay the tuition immediately, he also spent sixty-seven fen to buy a brand new

---

* Being a State employee, as opposed to being an ordinary member of a Production Brigade, meant one received rations of food, cooking oil, gas, etc.

bookbag for Dregs. Fifth Grandfather selected a pencil from Picked-Up's stock of goods and put it inside the bag.

Dregs went to school. In his first semester at grade school he won the Certificate of Merit.

Little Jade looked at this Certificate and turned it over and over in her hands as she asked Culture, 'How is it you've studied all these years and never brought home something like this?'

Without deigning to look at it, Culture answered, 'That doesn't count for anything.'

'Then what does?' Little Jade came right back at him.

The two of them often exchanged sallies like that, as equals. Bao Yanshan's wife saw this, and slowly she came to realize its significance. At night, with her head on the pillow, she talked it over with her man.

'Little Jade's seventeen – time to have them married.'

Shortly after that, Little Jade disappeared. After cutting a final bundle of wheat one day, she said to the others, 'You go along first. I'm going to wash my handkerchief in the creek.' She did not return.

CHAPTER 25

With the proliferation of literary magazines in China, Bao Renwen began to send manuscripts in all directions. 'Collected Works' had long since been taken apart and mailed off – as soon as a piece went off he gained another fragment of hope.

As a result, his days were so full of hope that he hardly had time for work. The weeds were prospering in the 3.4 *mou* that had been allocated to his family, while the seedlings were noticeably fewer than anyone else's. Even Second Aunt was doing better. There was some doubt in town about just what Bao Renwen had sown. To ask for help, his mother walked miles to a country shrine to burn a stick of incense. This folk-shrine had long since been destroyed but, convinced that the Buddha of the place was still alive, she stuck the incense into the ground in front of a nearby tree.

Around this time, the same classmate who was a typist in the Propaganda Department sent Bao Renwen some good news: the Province was planning to hold a Writers' Conference. This meant that a lot of writers would come together and enjoy themselves while expounding to each other on literature. The conference was to convene in the provincial capital, and then move to Bao Mountain for relaxation.

Like magazines, tourism was booming in China – any place with some history to its name was singled out as a place to see. Baotown could certainly be said to have history. It was even reported that on top of the mountain there was some kind of footprint, left by Baotown's founder as he surveyed the dam. There was also a cave with a stone table and chairs inside, used by the founder when he governed the area. It was said the authorities were going to set up a 'Tourist Attraction' there, although at the moment there was only a shack with someone selling tea. The place was definitely rustic – perhaps the writers had grown tired of their ivory towers and wanted to sample the flavour of a wilder place.

In any event, writers were going to come to Bao Mountain.

The county had been instructed by the province to put the place in order and to spruce it up. The local Writers' Association (even counties had Writers' Associations now) planned an occasion for the visiting writers to meet the local writers, to give 'grass-roots literature' guidance and inspiration. Notices went up: buy your ticket for the event. Within two days the tickets were completely sold out, an indication of the new popularity of literature.

Bao Renwen's classmate bought him a ticket, and he began looking forward to the day long before the event. The time dragged by. The classmate then sent a messenger with the news that at the last moment the conference had been cancelled. It seemed the writers were not coming to Bao Mountain after all: some were going to Xishuangbanna,* others to Jiuzhaigou,† others even planned to go to Tibet. Compared with these places, Bao Mountain was apparently not sufficiently wild.

* In Yunnan.
† In Western Sichuan.

81

All Bao Renwen could do was keep waiting and hoping, hoping for something that never seemed to happen.

Every day as he worked in the family plot of land his mind was full of conflicting worries and hopes. He thought of how old he was getting, how uncertain writing seemed to be as an occupation, how he did not have a family yet, although the days were relentlessly passing. What was waiting for him at the end of each flat, tasteless day? And what was waiting at the end of all these days? He wished he could jump over the next few years to see his splendid future. Then again, it might be miserable – he was in a quandary about whether the days should go slowly or fast.

Next to his field was the field of Bao Yanchuan's family. Every day Bao Yanchuan's widow brought her eleven-year-old son to the fields with her to work. Before the sun rose and long after it had set she toiled away, while the lazy boy, regrettably, either watched or played. For meals, she gnawed on hard flatbread that her eight-year-old daughter brought her at noon. She would wash the bread down with a ladle of cold water and then go back to work.

'Doing all right there by yourself?' Bao Renwen called out to her every day.

'No problem,' she would answer, knowing that there was no one to help her if she could not make it alone. As soon as the land was redistributed and put into the people's own hands it was as though a mad frenzy had come over them – some worked so hard they even wanted to sleep in the fields. Little thought was given to anything but one's individual plot and what one could make out of it.

Nevertheless, every few days Bao Renwen would notice a strong-looking outsider working in the neighbouring field. He did not look like a hired hand, and Second Aunt clearly treated him like a brother. It was equally clear that he did not treat her like a stranger. Moreover, he was willing to work hard, unlike any hired hand, and it had not been possible to find a hired hand in years. If there had been one available, Second Aunt could not have paid him.

82

The man was twenty years old at most. He seemed conscientious, always coming in the afternoon and working straight through till dark. Once, as he straightened up from work and looked around, he noticed Bao Renwen observing him from the neighbouring field. His teeth, when he smiled, were white as ivory, and Bao Renwen recognized the young man who had come through that day with the pedlar's pole.

This young man and Second Aunt were familiar to a surprising degree: Bao Renwen saw him carefully dab out something Second Aunt had got in her eyes; and he saw Second Aunt take a splinter out of the young man's hand. When Second Aunt wanted to smoke, the young man struck a match for her; when he smoked, Second Aunt struck a match for him. He called her 'Second Aunt', and she called him 'Little Brother'. The children called him 'Uncle'. It was difficult to make out just what the relationship was, but Bao Renwen found it all intensely interesting. The days went by so uneventfully that they were hard to endure – watching these two at least helped relieve the tedium.

CHAPTER 26

One day, the young man was peacefully hoeing Second Aunt's field when a crowd of people stormed up to him. Leading the crowd, with his shoulder pole held high, was Bao Yanshan. When he brandished this weapon the mob closed in, roughly knocking the young man to the ground. They were on him in an instant then, kicking and hitting, while he tried to curl up to protect his head.

Second Aunt saw this from a distance as she approached balancing two full pails of water. She came charging across the field, without taking time to put the pails down. They soon overturned and the water went splashing out – she tripped, stood and ran again, shouting all the while, 'Beat up on me! If you must beat someone, beat up on me!'

When she reached the mob she tried to pull Bao Yanshan away, who turned to kick her and replied, 'We'll beat you as well!'

The kick knocked her to her knees, but she stumbled up and came forward again. She grabbed his knees this time, begging, 'Older Brother, spare his life!'

Bao Yanshan could not help but put down his pole for a

second as he drew a long breath and looked around at the others. Then he yelled, 'You shameless hussy, you even have the nerve to ask for leniency for him!' He threw her off.

She spun around and immediately grabbed onto the young man, yelling into the mob, 'I seduced him, there was nothing he could do! I tricked him, he's not to blame!'

A wave of harder blows rained down on the two of them. Second Aunt and the young man held each other tightly then, without making a sound. No matter how the mob kicked, or beat, or yelled, the two of them were silent. At length the mob wore itself out and, after one final kick, departed. Somebody yelled back, 'If we catch you around this town again you won't get off so easy next time.'

Second Aunt and Picked-Up lay clinging to each other on the ground, motionless, as though already dead. Only after everyone had moved off into the distance did they begin to stir.

Picked-Up cried, 'Second Aunt, I've done you wrong, ruined your good name: beat me, beat me!'

'It's not your fault.' She rearranged her clothes as she answered, and her eyes were dry as a bone.

'I've brought this all on you, Second Aunt.'

'No, Picked-Up, I brought it on you.'

'I'd better go away and never come back.'

'If you want to, then go.' Second Aunt looked bitterly at him.

He stood and started off, then turned and knelt down to face her, head hanging down.

'What, not going?'

'How are you ever going to hoe this field alone if I leave?'

'I can hoe.'

'Well . . . then I'm going.' He looked sadly up at her and did not make a move.

'You know your pedlar's pole got smashed — what are you going to use to do business?'

'I can fix things.'

The two of them were silent for a while, thinking as they stared at the ground. Finally, Second Aunt said slowly and gravely, 'Picked-Up . . .'

'I'm listening, Second Aunt.'

'If . . . you're not ashamed of my being so old, and if you don't mind the children, you, you . . . then don't go!' Having said this much, she jerked her head and looked away.

Picked-Up lifted his eyes to look at her and a radiant happiness seemed to flow from them. He was choking with tears as he called out, 'Second Aunt!'

'I'm not Second Aunt to you any more.'

'All right.'

'I'm "Mother".'

'All right.'

Second Aunt slowly turned her head back to look at him, and she smiled now through her own tears. Picked-Up smiled back at her. Two pairs of swollen eyes in bloody faces saw each other through the refraction of tears. Both were grinning like fools.

Picked-Up did stay on in her house, but he was scared to death of being found out. How could he fool these people, when all of Bao Yanshan's own brothers were searching for him?

He paid a call on the troop leader, who was no longer troop leader but mayor. Now that the land had been redistributed, his title was different and his scope of jurisdiction had been reduced. He definitely could not, he said, have anything to do with this matter – he could not handle the Bao family; in fact, he felt that this whole matter was unmanageable. It was the first shameful thing to happen in Baotown in the past hundred years. He added that it had certainly made the people angry.

Picked-Up was a large man, not something you could easily hide, like a pouch of tobacco or a pair of shoes. It was not long before he was seen again and thrashed. After the beating this time he picked up his feet and ran. Second Aunt shouted to him in the distance, 'Picked-Up, run towards the township!'

This one sentence gave him an idea, and he turned in the opposite direction, heading for the administrative seat of the county. He covered the two or three miles in what seemed like one bound. In the township the case was given an impartial ruling: according to such and such lines in the marriage law it was legal for widows to remarry. A man coming to live in the woman's house after marriage was also legal.

Now that Picked-Up had a legal standing, he no longer had to hide from people. His legality did not, however, mean he was free from ridicule. Even little three-year-olds dared to throw dirt on Picked-Up's head. The name of Feng had been inserted into the immaculate line of Bao. It was said, moreover, that this particular Feng was not very clean himself – the family tree of Picked-Up was none too clear. This all made popular support very difficult to obtain. A calabash had been stuck into a basket of gourds: how were the folk of Baotown expected to ignore it?

The relative ages of Picked-Up and Second Aunt were yet another matter. There was considerable whispering, but this was nothing new to Picked-Up – he had grown up feeling rejected and had grown oblivious to it. After drifting for these past years he finally had a place to call home; it did not occur to him that Second Aunt might not be an appropriate wife. Passing the days with an older or younger woman was still passing the days. Besides, to him Second Aunt was mother, wife, sister, everything.

He felt supremely content, he fattened up and seemed to grow another foot in height. He was strong and healthy, and now took care of all the work in the field.

CHAPTER 27

'And now, the weather broadcast for this evening and tomorrow: this evening, cloudy with some rain, a light drizzle tending to showers, with heavy rain in some areas tending to thunderstorms.

'Tomorrow's forecast is for moderate to heavy rain. Appropriate flood control measures must be taken by the relevant departments . . .'

As a result of this, the county set up a flood-control command centre.

The township set up a flood-control command centre.

Baotown also set up a flood-control command centre.

CHAPTER 28

The rain came down in buckets – you could have washed your feet in it just by sitting in the doorway and holding them out. Several houses had already collapsed in the hollow to the west.

The head of the county came down to Baotown to have a look.

The head of the township came down to Baotown to have a look.

The mayor ran all over town getting people together to go up the mountain. There they set up a large tent that had been issued by the county.

Then in the distance the sky lightened and slowly the rain slackened – enough to make people think they had seen the worst of it this time. Just as everyone was relaxed and sitting down to lunch, a roar came from the west of the mountain – it was like thunder, but without the rolling intermittency of thunder. It came in one continuous noise, like thunder all pulled together.

'Run!'

Bowls were thrown down as everybody ran towards the east. Earlier in the year the township had organized a group of men to make a stone road – this year there would not be any sinking in the mud. This year, they intended to beat the flood.

Bao Bingde's wife had been lucid lately, but at this critical moment she chose to have a relapse. She began to dash madly about, her hair in a wild halo around her head. When Bao Bingde chased her, she sprinted in the direction of the flood, lifting her feet high and running like the wind. When he finally caught her, he could not hold her down. Several men came to help, and grabbed her while he tied her up. Then they sat her on his back; he gripped her legs around his waist.

Even bound she struggled, biting his shoulder until she drew blood. He clenched his teeth but did not let go, then started for the mountain in the east.

All of Bao Yanshan's family had made it to the stone road. It was not until they paused to count heads that they realized one was missing. Dregs was not there.

'Dregs!' His mother began to shout.

'He went to take some flatbread over to Fifth Grandfather – he could be over there,' Culture finally remembered.

'Father, you go back and find him!' Bao Yanshan's wife screamed.

The water was already up to his crotch.

Bao Yanshan headed back towards town, and asked every person he met along the way, 'Have you seen Dregs?'

'No, haven't seen him,' somebody said.

'Yes, I saw him coming along with Fifth Grandfather,' another said.

Bao Yanshan's heart skipped a beat, but he kept asking as he went, 'Seen Dregs?'

'No, haven't seen him,' somebody said.

'Saw him helping Fifth Grandfather,' another said.

The floodwater rose and was now over Bao Yanshan's waist. He faced it and thought, 'We're not going to make it if we don't get out now.'

Those bringing up the rear came even with him and yelled, 'What the hell are you doing here?'

'Looking for Dregs!'

'He passed a long time ago, dragging Fifth Grandfather with him!'

Bao Yanshan turned around then, and followed the others back up the mountain.

From her seat on his back, Bao Bingde's wife struggled fiercely, fighting to get down, fighting to reach the water. Bao Bingde could barely keep his balance. 'Don't you want to live?' he yelled.

She suddenly snapped the rope – her two free hands now grabbed her man's head and wrenched it backwards.

'You bitch!' Bao Bingde shouted helplessly. His feet were slipping, his centre of gravity was going. With a supreme effort he made himself stand firm. He knew that loosening his hold by just a little would mean that both of them were lost. The water was already at his chest.

She finally let go of his hair and he could breathe more easily. He had not drawn a full breath, however, when she twisted her body around violently, as though wanting to look back over the darkening flood. He staggered, loosened his grip for an instant – and the crazy woman was gone.

A vast, even sheet of water: no person in sight.

The water had rushed after the people of Baotown in vain as they tramped up the stone road. Because of the road, they had won. From the top of the mountain they looked over where they had been: where was their town? It had become a sea, an ocean – turned into a single floating wooden tub.

The mayor counted heads. They were all there except for the crazy woman, except for Dregs and Fifth Grandfather.

'Dregs!' he shouted.

'Dregs!' screamed Bao Yanshan's wife, putting her whole body into it.

Bao Yanshan said to everyone, 'Didn't you say you'd seen him together with Fifth Grandfather?'

'No, I didn't – I never said that!' was the answer.

Getting desperate, he flared up, 'But you said you'd seen

him! You said you'd seen him dragging along Fifth Grand-father!'

Everybody said they had not seen him, and Bao Yanshan could not remember who exactly had said that they had. This was not surprising, for people often do not see or hear right in emergencies.

Bao Yanshan's wife started back down the mountain to look, but several of the women restrained her. 'You won't make it – don't forget, water and fire have no feelings.'

'Dregs! . . . My son! . . .' All she could do was weep, and her weeping soon had the whole group of women in tears.

'Stop that!' the mayor ordered with authority. Since the land had been redistributed and he had been made a mere mayor, there were few occasions when he could take the lead. 'Those men who can swim, come with me.'

After selecting about ten men he had them cut down several small trees to build rafts. The group soon went down the mountain carrying these.

The rafts floated on the water, floated out over Baotown. Instead of a town now, there was nothing but a wide waste of water. Looking out to the horizon you could not see its end; the only things in sight were some boards and a few shoe soles.

'Dregs!' They yelled in chorus, the sound moving without obstruction in four directions, soon dissipating so that they themselves hardly heard their own yells.

'Fifth Grandfather!' There was no response. Their call was like a needle dropped into the water – so tiny it did not even make a splash.

The rafts floated aimlessly. There was no here or there, no way even to tell direction.

The rafts floated; a bird on the water flew away. In the distance Bao Mountain looked considerably less high.

'What's that?' somebody yelled.

'Couldn't be a person, could it?'

In the hazy distance was what looked like a tassel of grass, and on that crouched what looked like the shadow of a person.

All the rafts rowed toward it. When they were near, they realized this was the top of the old willow tree, the highest tree on the highest point in town. In the branches huddled Fifth Grandfather. He was pointing at the base of the tree and croaking, 'Dregs! Dregs!'

Under the branches was water; in the distance was Bao Mountain, dark and sombre.

The men tore off their clothes, and one after another dived into the water. One after another they struggled down, to emerge empty-handed and breathless, then they went down again. They kept it up for at least an hour. In the end, Picked-Up, with one desperate plunge, disappeared for a long time. When he emerged, he could not speak, but only gasped in lungfuls of air. Down he went again, and again it was a long time before he came up. When he did come up, his arms were embracing Dregs.

The men on the rafts frantically hauled the two of them aboard. They laid Dregs out straight – his eyes were shut and he had long since ceased to breathe. His mouth was slightly curved up, as though he were still laughing. Someone suddenly noticed that Fifth Grandfather too had breathed his last.

The return trip of the rafts had added an old one and a young one, neither of whom was able to speak. Ten dripping men rowed slowly back to the mountain. As they came in sight, there were shouts to welcome them back.

An old one and a young one lay side by side on a raft, their faces peaceful, as though they were only sleeping. The brow of the old one was smooth and unworried – he had not looked so tranquil since the death of Society. The young one too looked strangely serene, and his face was rosier than when he had been alive.

Bao Yanshan's wife stared: not a word came out. All the townsfolk came around her, encouraging her to cry, saying that it would be better if she cried it out.

The mayor related to everyone how they had first seen Fifth Grandfather, and how they in turns had dived down to look for Dregs.

Picked-Up then haltingly gave his description. 'I was feeling around and I came across something . . . soft. Then I felt around, and found . . . a little hand. My heart went numb. I tried to pull him up, but I couldn't budge him. His arms . . . were wrapped around the tree trunk, locked on to it . . .'

Everybody exclaimed, 'If Dregs had gone up the tree first he wouldn't have died.'

'If Dregs had run for his own life, he would have made it.'

'Naturally! The legs of the little ones are fast – our two were way ahead of us.'

'Dregs died for Fifth Grandfather.'

'This child . . .' Trembling a little, the same Bao Yanrong who had fought the battle of Mengliang-gu lifted up his big, scarred thumb and said, 'This child is a model example.'

'My child!' Bao Yanshan's wife finally cried out, and then nobody could keep from crying.

With eyes peacefully closed, Dregs slept on top of the mountain. Below him heaved a wide ocean. Bao Bingde knelt to face that white expanse, which somewhere covered his wife, and he too quietly cried.

The day slowly darkened as men, women and children grew quiet, surrounding a pile of flatbread and rolls that the county had sent by boat. Not even a child took one.

As the day darkened, the water seemed to grow brighter.

CHAPTER 29

The flood had been the worst in a century, yet in the most vulnerable part of the county, in Baotown, only three had died. And at that, they had been a lunatic, an old man and a child – indeed, the child could have lived, but died trying to rescue the old man.

When the water receded it was time to have the funeral. It was agreed that Dregs could not be sent off in the normal way for children – although he was young, his humanity had been that of an adult. To wrap him in a mat would be a disgrace: Dregs would go to his grave in a wooden coffin.

Men went to buy boards, women went to buy cloth. He was to be dressed in a blue student's uniform and a lined jacket, his feet were for the first time to wear new white running shoes. Never since landing on this earth had Dregs worn a whole new jacket – they had all been hand-me-downs, torn and patched, from his older brothers. Dregs was to be sent off properly or nobody in Baotown would feel right.

Everybody in town joined the funeral procession. People even came from neighbouring towns – they had heard of the child who died for an old widower, they knew that Baotown had produced a child of exceptional kindness and compassion. The procession was over two hundred people long, two hundred adults sending one small child down the road. Baotown only recognized kindness: it did not respect wealth or fear force. The adults of Baotown joined together to pay their respects to a child.

The children of Baotown were left behind: children were never allowed to walk behind a casket. Only adults could attend a funeral.

Women whispered and cried among themselves, and the wind took the soft sounds off into the distance. The Mayor led, followed by men with lowered heads. Those carrying the casket all bore the name 'Yan'; they carried a child of the generation all bearing the name 'Ren'.

The wet earth was dark and silent, and seemed to lick hungrily at the feet of the mourners. A long, crooked line of footprints was left in the procession's wake.

The group made its way to the side of the big ditch, where a grave had been dug. The casket was lowered into the ground. The mayor scooped on the first handful of earth, the oldest man in town the second. 'Not worth it, to die for an old end-of-the-liner,' he muttered.

Wind sighed through a small stand of trees across the ditch. Deep green water, full to the top of the banks, reflected the scene. The earth was shovelled on until it became a small mound, and this mound too became a swaying image in the water.

Bao Yanshan stamped twice on the mound, cleared his throat, and said, 'Child, we didn't do right by you, never even gave you a decent meal.' Tears that had almost stopped started up again, and the water seemed to join in, wrinkling into waves. The image of the mound swayed back and forth.

The sky darkened a moment, as though the sun, still high, were going down. Bao Mountain stood solemn and respectful, guarding a little world that was deep in sorrow.

That evening no stove cooked dinner in Baotown, not a

single chimney emitted any smoke. Unable to bear the crying of the women, the men retreated to the cow-pen where they smoked in silence, leaning against its walls. The old ballad singer sang a halting tune:

十 千 '"Ten" with a line on top reads "one thousand".
The Song Emperor took his lady one thousand miles.
九 力 "Nine" with its tail turned in means power and strength.
Yan Zhang of the Song had boundless powers.

人 入 Turn "ren" around it becomes "ru".
Ren Chang Hui teamed up with Yang Tian Lang.'

Bao Erye softly asked the old revolutionary, 'Has Bao Bingde's wife been found?'

The old man's eyes did not move from the ballad singer as he answered, 'No.'

'That's strange.'

'They've been in the ditch from one end to the other, looking for her.' His eyes never left the ballad singer.

'That woman, maybe . . . strange . . .'

The old revolutionary only quietly listened.

五 伍 'Add a "man" to "five" and it is still read "wu".
Wu Tze Xu did battle
And crossed the Yangtze River.

四 㕚 "Four" with a line on top becomes a "xi".
Xi Liang fought the dynasties year after year.'

CHAPTER 30

Bao Renwen wrote a turgid piece about Picked-Up and Second Aunt and sent it to the local radio station – he called it *Lofty Love*.

He wrote how Picked-Up was not bothered by Second Aunt's age and children, and how Second Aunt was unconcerned about Picked-Up's lack of family, house or land. Since theirs was the loftiest of loves, they came together as companions. They worked hard together by day, and under a lamp at night they made plans to get rich.

Within a week this piece had been broadcast. It was an immediate sensation, drawing people from miles around to get a glimpse of the couple. It did not change Picked-Up's status in Baotown, however, where he was still referred to as one who had gone to his wife's home, rather than having her properly come to his.

Adjoining Second Aunt's land was a plot belonging to Bao Renyuan. In the clear light of day Bao Renyuan openly ploughed up a large strip that rightfully belonged to her. Picked-Up did not dare say a word about it. Without a man, Second Aunt had not been cheated – now that she had a man, she was.

What was worse, when Second Aunt was single she had stood her own with anybody – she had not minded speaking up and saying what was on her mind. Now that she had a man, it was as though she had developed some defect – she kept thinking that this man of hers was not someone of whom she could be proud. As a result, she was slightly ashamed and much less sure of herself.

None the less, it was clear that having any man at all was better than having none. With a man around your mind was at ease, and the day's work did not tire you out so much. She sincerely appreciated Picked-Up, but at the same time she had the persistent feeling that she was taking care of him, putting him up. So when she called him to wake up, for instance, it was hard to avoid having an edge of impoliteness in her voice.

'Picked-Up, I can see the bottom of the water barrel!'

Picked-Up would go fetch water.

'Picked-Up, start the fire!'

Picked-Up would start the fire.

'Picked-Up, the pot's boiling over.'

Picked-Up would damp the fire.

'Picked-Up, the pig's running away.'

'I'm just eating my breakfast,' he would say.

'Can't you eat while you chase him?'

So he would set off, chomping on his flatbread, calling to the pig through a mouthful of food.

Gradually getting used to this, Picked-Up allowed her to order him about. He did not mind being told what to do, what he did mind was her complaining. From time to time when his duties had not been executed just right, she would start in, and then it would be endless. Although Picked-Up had gone to his wife's house instead of the other way around, he was still a man, and he still had a temper. When it was aroused, then the two of them would fight. Unlike others, they fought behind a closed door with their voices down – if one had been beaten to death no one outside would have known. When they were through arguing and fighting, the door would open, and it would be as if nothing at all had happened. At night the two would again be warm and cuddly, doing what in marriage ought to be done.

One thing that secretly disturbed Picked-Up was the fact that in this household he would never be master. This was Second Aunt's home and whenever there was some matter to decide, people would go looking for her, and never come to him. If they had come to him, he would immediately, if the truth be known, have gone to her – but they did not come to him first, and this omission rankled.

Second Aunt herself neglected to talk things over with him. One example was the issue of having Little Three go to school. If she had asked him, he would naturally have given permission – her children were, after all, her own, and he did not want to be mean. But she did not ask, as though he were not the man in the household, and this made Picked-Up distinctly upset. This was something that was hard to discuss, though, so his unhappiness appeared in the guise of other matters.

'Why is this porridge so watery? Is it just boiled water, or what?'

'I put in an extra half-ladle of water – just take it or leave it!'

'How can I do a full day's work on this? Even hired hands have to be fed properly.' Picked-Up thumped down the bowl.

'When you were wandering around as a pedlar you were lucky to get this much to eat.' Second Aunt's lips tightened as she said it.

When you hit someone it is best not to hit the face; when you criticize, it is best not to touch a raw nerve. This sentence of hers hit home, and Picked-Up immediately took the bowl up again and broke it.

Second Aunt could break bowls too, and she could make a hellish scene doing it – but she did not forget to close the door first.

To fight once in a while – naturally that did not mean anything. But as the fights began to mount up, they began to mean a little something. One by one they accumulated until they had become a large something – stashed away inside, they formed a knot of unhappiness. Of course, unhappy days had always outnumbered the happy ones, and there were those who had more, but then again there were those who had less.

Not long after Baotown broadcast their story, the county station also picked it up and broadcast it. Picked-Up and Second Aunt felt mortified, but at the same time a little proud. Famous now, they began to feel that they should not argue so much, but deciding this was a different thing from doing it. They only closed the door more tightly, and yelled more softly.

When Bao Renwen heard that the county station had broadcast his story he was overjoyed. This marked the pinnacle of his literary career up to now. He was not sure why he thought so, but he had the impression that all county broadcasts were eventually published in the famous *Literary World*. Half a month went by without news from *Literary World*, but Renwen was too embarrassed to approach them, and in the end decided to forget about it. Instead, he revised the story and made it into a novel, and mailed it off to a provincial journal. After that, he again enjoyed unlimited hope. As for Picked-Up and Second Aunt arguing in their room, that was not his responsibility.

CHAPTER 31

After Dregs' death, Culture felt that his mother found an unusual number of things wrong with him. In almost everything she felt it necessary to compare him to his brother. He felt it odd that for each of his shortcomings Dregs seemed to have a virtue. By every one of these many shortcomings his mother would be reminded of Dregs' goodness. This would start her crying and, once started, her crying would go on for hours.

'Culture, come massage my shoulders a minute, will you?'

'I'm feeding the pig right now.'

This alone would make his mother cry. 'If Dregs were here, I wouldn't even have to ask, he'd massage me right away. As soon as I came in the door Dregs would always bring a basin of water for me to wash my face with. I never needed to lift a finger. Oh Dregs, you left us too soon!'

This went on until her crying began to exasperate people. Culture began to suffocate with a feeling of contained frustration. He too felt badly, and not only about Dregs. The death of his little brother naturally made him feel as though a chunk of his own heart had been cut out. His little brother was undeniably good – despite being younger, he had done what he could for Culture. If he had not, Dregs could have gone to school a year earlier and won a couple more 'Superior Student Awards'. But the grief had to be put aside some time: the dead were dead and the living had to go on living. The living, moreover, could not help thinking about others who were living.

Specifically, he thought about Little Jade. Only after she left did he come to realize that she liked him, and that he also liked her. Only now were her hopes for him clear, and this too depressed Culture.

His older brother was also morose: his reason was that he did not have a wife. He was now twenty-six years old, and thinking of little else than having a woman.

What was bothering Culture had nothing to do with a wife. He could not even think about marriage until his older brother was settled – he only wished his brother would hurry up and choose anyone except Little Jade. Whoever it was to be, let it not be Little Jade, dear God, anyone but Little Jade. Please, Little Jade, do not come back.

But Culture could not keep himself from hoping she would come back. Down at The Lake, he would imagine her running over and pushing him onto his back; by the side of the well he would remember her springing up and grabbing his pole: 'Give me back *December*!' He remembered giving back that other song, and how she had instantly learnt it. 'You really should be going to school.' Culture sighed – he had discovered that Little Jade's hope for him was also her hope for herself. She was the one who really should have been going to school. With family circumstances as they were, he had not been able to go himself. What point was there in even thinking about Little Jade's going?

He thought about school, thought about reading. He often visited Bao Renwen, to borrow books, to talk. He wondered why he felt comfortable with Renwen now, when he found he could not talk to anyone else.

103

'Brother Wen, you can't be thinking of going on forever as a bachelor.'

'I can't live my life the way everybody else here does,' Bao Renwen answered. To others, the answer would have been incomprehensible, but Culture understood him perfectly.

'Not easy, is it.'

'I'm not scared of how hard anything is, I'm just scared of not having hope.'

'Do you have any hope right now?'

'If you think you do, then you do. If you think you don't, then you don't.' Bao Renwen smiled ever so slightly, and Culture knew exactly what he meant.

'What you're doing right now doesn't necessarily mean you'll be doing it for a lifetime – isn't that right, Brother Wen?'

'Just depends on whether you yourself feel what you're doing is worthwhile.'

'Each has his own way of doing things, right?'

'Don't look at what others do – just mind yourself, that's the thing.'

'And don't mind either what others think about you, right?'

The two of them could sit crosslegged and go back and forth like this the whole night long. Every time he emerged from Bao Renwen's dilapidated old room, Culture felt his cares had lightened.

One night, as he was going home from Bao Renwen's house and had almost reached his own door, a person dashed out from the shadows and suddenly blocked his way. A pair of jet black shiny eyes transfixed him: it was Little Jade. He nearly cried out but she quickly covered his mouth, then grabbed his hand and ran behind the house and down the bank. Her hand was sweaty and hot – he gripped it hard.

The two ran until they had burrowed deep into a sorghum field, then they stopped and stood still, looking at each other. Little Jade was considerably thinner – her eyes were bigger now and a fathomless black. The moonlight flicked shadows of sorghum across her face. They made flashes of light and dark as though the scene were in a dream.

'Where did you go?' Culture wanted to caress her face, and although he did not dare, the very thought made him tingle.

She stared back at him without answering.

Remembering her danger, he was suddenly alarmed: 'Why did you come back?'

'I came back for you.' As she said it, the tears came, great big tears, falling down on the sorghum leaves.

Now it was Culture's turn not to speak.

'Didn't you want me to come back?' she asked.

'I was about to go looking for you.'

In an instant she had thrown her arms around his neck, and only then did Culture dare embrace her. The moon softly watched them, then turned away, then glanced again. The dew came up as the sorghum heads lightly brushed against each other in the breeze. A fall cricket began to sing. The shadows of leaves swayed back and forth over her body and his body. The dew felt cool and sweet.

'Jade, don't go. If you must, let's go together.'

'I came back just to hear that one sentence from you. Now that you've said it, I won't worry.'

'I won't worry either, Jade,' Culture murmured.

'I only wanted to hear you say it,' she whispered.

'You must have had terrible thoughts,' he replied.

'Yours must have been worse,' she said.

'I thought you had come to scold me, to beat me.'

The two of them quietly laughed, and quietly cried. The moonbeams gently watched them, the sorghum leaves gently caressed them.

CHAPTER 32

Bao Bingde remarried. This time, he married a pockmarked woman from a few miles away. Her face was pitted and her body was large and coarse, but for his purpose a big woman was just what he wanted. Bao Yanshan's wife had acted as go-between: it took just one word and the matter was all arranged. If she was to be a bride, the sooner the better – a date was set without further ado and she arrived.

The crazy one had died only three months before, but everybody in Baotown understood and sympathized: these two could not afford to wait. 3.4 *mou* of redistributed land lay waiting for attention; without somebody at home to cook, it was not going to get it. More to the point, Bao Bingde was already over forty and ready to hug a son.

Everybody was invited to the celebration. Bao Renwen made an excuse, though, and stayed alone at home. Sitting in his broken-down room, he listened to the sounds of the finger-guessing game, with drinks as forfeits, issuing from Bao Bingde's house. He felt distracted and listless, as though he had lost something. He was lonely. A solitary lamp accompanied his lonely soul, and he began to wonder just what he was living for.

It seemed even more uproarious over there all of a sudden. Perhaps they had started to tease the groom. Then everything quietened down again – the new bride was probably singing a song. Silence reigned for a while, until the merriment began anew – Bao Renwen listened intently to what was going on. He was taken by surprise when the door suddenly opened, and Culture stepped in to have a talk.

'Have you seen the bride?' Bao Renwen asked.

'I glanced at her,' Culture said.

'What do you think?'

'A face full of holes.' Culture sat on the edge of the bed and began to flip through a book.

Bao Renwen lay back on the bed again. Cradling his head in his hands, he stared up at the black recesses of the eaves.

'My mom started crying again, thinking about Dregs. Seems she and Dregs sat on a bench together this same time last year, splitting sorghum stalks.'

'Dregs was a model example – even Bao Yanrong, who was honourable himself, said so.'

'Brother Wen, couldn't you write Dregs' story into an article somehow?'

'Write about Dregs?' Bao Renwen sat up.

'Dregs didn't die for himself, he died for Bao Fifth Grandfather – that's something to write about.'

'Yes . . . it is. I could write a kind of reportage piece on it,' Bao Renwen said softly to himself.

'My brother had a rough time. And he was only nine years old, hadn't even grown up, when he died.'

'Not very old, but what he did had a stroke of greatness in it.'

'When my mother starts crying she goes on and on, how they never gave him a decent meal when he was alive. Now that there's a good harvest and plenty to eat this year, he's gone.'

Bao Renwen sat on the side of the bed and felt around on the floor with his feet for his shoes. His whole body seemed to be shivering with delicious tremors. 'The inspiration's coming,' he said. 'Yes, the inspiration's come.' Grabbing pen and paper, he was soon oblivious to Culture.

Culture similarly paid no attention to him. Changing places, he took off his shoes, lay on his back on the bed and cradled his head in his hands. He stared up at the black recesses of the eaves.

Would Little Jade be able to come tonight, or not? With all the festivities, and people carrying lanterns, he worried that even past midnight it would not be safe. She was doing part-time work for a family a few miles outside of town – she had said she would come over as soon as she was finished. He was to wait, every night, until the moon was at its highest, and then go out behind the house to keep watch for her. They had agreed to grit their teeth and wait until Construction found a wife. Then Little Jade would return and marry Culture.

Although she had never married Construction, or even been registered to marry him, absolutely everybody in town regarded her as Construction's wife. Culture was looked on as merely her Little Uncle. She did not dare show her face until Construction had a family.

Bao Yanshan's wife was distressed by this matter of Construction. She knew that the reason he could not find a wife was that he had no real home to offer. After going through the flood of a century, one section of their three-room hut was collapsing – great clods of earth were always falling to the floor. There was no telling when the whole thing might come down, burying the members of the household underneath.

She and her man talked it over: this year they would take all of the harvest, except the seed grain, and sell it in order to build another house. What they were going to eat was a problem they had not yet resolved. Every night the two of them turned on their pillows like pancakes, tossing and fretting until the roosters called out to the dawn.

Culture looked up at the rafters – there seemed to be a black hole behind them so dark you could not see inside. After a good deal of staring he felt his very being had been absorbed into the bottomless black hole.

Slowly, the town became quiet. People passed the door on their way home; the sound of their voices punctuated the night.

'Who cares about her face? If she can bear children, she's fine.'

'From the looks of her middle and her rump, I'll bet she can have a whole litter of them.'

'Damn, it's cold!'

The footsteps stomped along muddy earth, and then were gone.

The moon reached its zenith.

CHAPTER 33

Second Aunt's elder son was now sixteen, a tall strapping boy with a dark face that refused to smile. While a year ago he still called Picked-Up 'Uncle', this year he called him nothing at all. If Picked-Up asked him to do anything, he ignored him. Second Aunt discussed everything with this son, to the exclusion of Picked-Up. This irked Picked-Up so much he finally decided to leave.

He found the pedlar's pole, and fixed its rack. Then he looked at the drum, took it in hand and softly gave it a tap: tock tock.

The sound was still crisp.

Picked-Up stood vacantly for a while, as though remembering something, but in the end he could not actually think of what it was. He tucked the pedlar's drum into his belt and balanced the pole on his shoulder. Then he left without saying a word to Second Aunt.

She cooked dinner, and waited for him to come home to eat. She waited and he did not come, waited and he still did not come. She walked out to the front of town and then out behind town and asked people if they had seen him: they said no. They had seen a pedlar, however, walking down the main road, who had looked like Picked-Up. She ran home then, and looked for the pole with its broken rack. When she could not find it, she understood.

'Am I worried that you won't come back?' she muttered to herself. 'You low-down thing!' Her face was tight as she poured porridge for herself and sat down and ate it. She scrubbed the pot, and then she went to bed. The wind blew outside, and with every gust her ears perked up: was that somebody knocking at the door? No, just the wind in the grasses. She hardly slept, but nobody came home in the night.

On the second day she got up early and went about doing what she needed to do. The third day was the same, but by the fourth day she could not concentrate. That night she wrapped the quilt around her shoulders, and sat up smoking and staring at the wall. As the sky lightened, she changed into her somewhat newer blue jacket, and out she went, having decided to go look for him.

'Mother, what are you doing? Going to look for that scum?' her son asked rudely.

'I'm going to look for your father, that's what I'm doing! You heartless little bastard,' she shouted at him, and although he did not say a word after that, she kept yelling. 'If it weren't for him you'd be dead long ago, if not by starving to death, then by working till you dropped. He's your father. Never mind that he's not much older than you are. He's still your father, and if I catch you not calling him Father, you'll see . . .' Second Aunt yelled, and as she did a lump came to her throat. She thought of the way Picked-Up looked when he ploughed the field: his broad back bare, with drops of sweat glistening on his shoulders, the waistband of his pants completely wet.

Picked-Up followed the wide road as he balanced his pole and walked along. It went up and over the mountain ahead and disappeared. He remembered one moonlit night when this road had also shone white before him, when a beetle-like shadow had slowly come over the hill, turning into a cart as it approached. A woman had been pushing the cart, and on it was the frame for a bed and a basket. In the basket was fabric, cotton wadding for a quilt, fruit and a box of cigarettes.

As he remembered, he lifted his sleeve and took a swipe at his nose.

When he got there, the town was quiet, with only old people and children about. He walked up to his old house, whose thatched roof seemed to have sunk closer to the ground. The mud brick walls had gradually settled with the rains, and moved earthward with their load of thatch and one rotten roofbeam. All around it stood shiny new homes, tiled from top to bottom.

The door was not locked. It had been left unlatched, but was stuck shut and hard to open. When he put his shoulder to it, it came completely off its hinges. The room was empty, the floor covered with shucked cornhusks. Sunlight filtered through the brick-hole, picking out circling clouds of dust. A one-burner stove, two beds, a board for a table and a summer cot were all that he saw as he stood with his head almost hitting the ceiling. Several children now crowded into the doorway, looking silently at him.

'Where's the person who lived here?' he asked.

'Gone,' the children answered.

'Where to?'

The children gazed at each other, then one slightly larger than the rest said, 'To the north.'

Picked-Up stood awhile, then walked out and put the door back in place. He latched it, and turned around to go. The sun was so bright that it was hard to open his eyes. It must have been the sun that made him so dizzy.

After a while he picked up his pole and set off again, walking past field after field with people working hard in them. He thought of Second Aunt's field, thought of it burnt hot by the sun, burnt so hot your feet were scorched and your heart was warmed. Thought of its stinking smell; thought how what you planted in that land you would reap. There was no tricking that land – you could not trick it in the slightest. And it, in turn, would not trick a man's honest labour. He thought of Second Aunt working in that field, her torn blouse flapping in the wind, revealing her two full breasts.

He walked slowly along, as his drum made a listless accompaniment: tock tock, tock tock.

As he entered another town, a housewife came up to buy thread. A young girl hurried over to choose some cloth. All sorts of hands were soon flying about his rack – he looked at them, and his heart was heavy. He waited patiently for them to make their selections, to buy or not to buy, then rearranged his goods, and shouldered his pole. Straightening his back, he was about to step forward when he froze. Not ten paces away from him stood a woman. Her face was covered with dirt and sweat, her hand was on her hip. She was glaring at him.

'Second . . . Second . . .' he began to say, then changed it to 'Mother'.

'Mother's dead! She was cast off by her man, she hung herself, she threw herself in a river, she hit her head on a rock at Bao Mountain and died!'

'Now, how could all that have happened . . .' Picked-Up smiled apologetically, but his insides felt as if he had just drunk a hot cup of strong tea.

'Her husband went to find a fancy lady! Went to find someone with high heels, a foreign lady with hair all permed into lion's curls! Went to find a young lady who had an apartment house to live in!'

'Now, how could that be?' Picked-Up approached, and raised his hand to touch her shoulder. Her fist knocked it away.

'Her man died, she's a widow, she remarried – off to the other side of the mountain, to far away!'

'Now, now . .' Picked-Up put the hand that had been knocked away on his own shoulder, which he rubbed.

'She had a whole tribe of children, had boys, girls, had tall ones, short ones, square ones, round ones . . .' Second Aunt herself could not help laughing, but immediately covered it up.

Picked-Up began to move off down the road. 'Where do you think you're going?' Second Aunt yelled after him.

'Going home!' Picked-Up answered.

'So where's your home? Do you still remember home?'

He did not dare move, and stood motionless, waiting to know what she meant.

'So you don't answer – have you died? Do you want to die? Do you want to stay out in the wilds and be eaten by dogs?'

Only then did he dare to make a move, and it was to follow her. He felt lighthearted. He asked himself, 'What was all the fuss about, anyway?' 'It wasn't anything,' he answered. As he walked he became happier and happier, until unthinkingly he was walking in front of her.

The sun shone down on the earth, the wind blew the willows in sweeping curves. A sparrow sang, the pedlar's drum seemed to laugh – tock tock, tock tock, tock tock. Walking along, he turned around and saw that Second Aunt was wiping away a tear. Dumbfounded, he said, 'What's this all about?'

'You heartless wretch!' Second Aunt now sniffled as she scolded him.

'It's true I went away, but now I'm coming back.'

'If I hadn't come looking for you, would you have come home?'

'If you hadn't looked, I would still have come back home.'

'You're lying.'

'Lightning strike me five times if I'm lying,' Picked-Up swore on oath. He looked at Second Aunt's tear-laden face, and felt his own throat get thick.

It was late by the time the two of them filed back into town. Second Aunt unlocked the door and as she entered the room, she ordered, 'Get the fire started!'

Picked-Up had not yet reached the stove when she yelled

again, 'The bottom of the water barrel's showing and you still haven't fetched the water.'

So Picked-Up stood up again and went to fetch the water.

CHAPTER 34

Bao Bingde did not know where he found so many things to say. Every night as soon as it was dark he would go to bed, and immediately begin talking to his new wife. He told her about the history of Baotown: how the founder had been a high official, so she should not look down on how poor they were today – people in Baotown had a proud heritage. He told her the sad story of his own private household: how his wife had gone crazy and tried to hang herself but not succeeded, how during the great flood she had fallen off his back and drowned. Until this day they had not been able to find so much as a hair from her head.

His wife listened quietly. Her pockmarks were invisible in the dark: all he knew was that there was a warm face pressed to his, that he could feel the eyebrows blink at long intervals. He knew that she was awake and listening to him.

Bao Bingde had always considered himself inarticulate. Before, several days at a stretch would pass without his saying a word. When he did say something, the sound of his voice frightened even himself. These days his monologues bothered him but he could not hold them back – it was as though the words had been stored up through the years and had been suffocating inside. Strange that talking seems to bring a person to life. Thinking back over the years, he did not know how his old self had had the energy to go on.

Her face pressed against his, her eyelashes measured a reassuring rhythm. She was awake, and she was listening to him.

She was already with child. Without even kneeling to listen to her stomach he knew that it was living and healthy. He felt that this woman was living solely to bring him children, that she was living one hundred per cent for him. Holding her as he slept, he felt secure.

There were times in the day when he was sitting on a bench, warming his feet in a pail of hot water and smoking, watching her work, that he could not help seeing the image of a slender figure, with a long black braid swinging as it dashed through a door. At those times he would feel a knife cutting through his heart. He believed that his first wife had intentionally jumped into the water, in order to make way for this woman, and to make way for himself. If they could only find her body and bury her properly, then he could visit from time to time, weed the grave, put more dirt on it and relieve his sadness. But she had hidden, not allowing him a square inch on which to place his grief. She had made room for him, but also asked him to make room for her.

Bao Bingde felt an aching, remorseless sorrow. But as soon as dark settled in and he wrapped himself around his woman, the words started pouring out again. In the back of his mind he seemed to hear someone singing, a reedy voice like the wind, coming from the sorghum fields out back. When he concentrated on it, it disappeared.

CHAPTER 35

Bao Renwen worked all night, until he had finished the re-portage piece on Dregs. Then, with huge energy, he made five, six, seven copies, and like an important bulletin dispatched them to major publications. He sent them to the province, the region and the county, to journals, newspapers, youth and children's magazines.

Autumn harvest came, and the grain was brought inside for storage. New Year came, and Bao Bingde's wife was big with child – it would not be long now.

Firecrackers were popping all over town.

That day, a jeep was seen coming down the road. It drove into town and asked the way to Bao Renwen's house. Finding he was not there it came right down to the fields to look for him.

In the distance, Bao Renwen watched the jeep stop. He watched two men get out and begin walking straight for him. Trampling down the new shoots, they marched closer and closer ... His heart beating wildly now, Renwen stopped work and put up his thatched sunscreen to wait. These were not men from around Baotown – one of them did not even seem to be from the region. The sun was behind them, and blinded his searching eyes.

The two marched closer and closer, step by step.

The men marched towards him, closer and closer, step by step.

Two men marched up to him and demanded, 'Are you Comrade Bao Renwen?'

'Yes,' he said, his voice sounding weak and shaky.

'This is Comrade Hu, a journalist from the regional *Morning Star News*.' The more local-looking man indicated the less local-looking man, then added, 'I'm from the county Cultural Office – my name is Wang.'

Comrade Hu immediately put out his hand to Bao Renwen. He was wearing glasses and looked young – but it was hard to tell the age of city people. After warmly shaking Bao Renwen's hand, he dragged him down to sit on the ground, as though he were the host and this land was his to offer.

They had come because of the reportage piece on Dregs. The manuscript had arrived, been scanned and then put aside. Now New Year* was here already and next month, March, was going to be 'Courtesy Month'. The leaders wanted them to publicize some model example, in order to complement the current propaganda campaign.† They had remembered Bao Renwen's piece of reportage and taken it out to look at it more closely. After a thorough reading, they felt it had traces of potential. In brief, it would do.

It was just that, how to say it, it would need some polishing. They wanted to enrich the part about Dregs taking care of Fifth Grandfather. One had to realize that the problem of old age was a worldwide dilemma – too many old people, who needed taking care of by the young. So they had sent Comrade Hu out to help Bao Renwen complete his piece.

* In the lunar calendar.
† The 'Four Beautifications and Five Spruce-Ups Campaign' of 1982–3, a campaign to combat incivility.

The matter was urgent: Bao Renwen would have to go back to the city with them today. They would have to work hard to get the piece ready for typesetting, in time to see it come out in the 1 March issue of the paper.

Bao Renwen listened to all this as though it were a duet being sung in paradise. 'Am I dreaming?' he asked himself, dizzy and weak all over. He found he could not even raise a tiny smile. He watched Comrade Hu's young face talking, but did not hear what he said: it was like a movie which has run into problems and has the picture but not the sound. Comrade Hu passed him a cigarette. Dazed, he took it and allowed Comrade Hu to light it for him without even saying thank you.

Finally, Comrade Hu stood up, patted the dirt off his rump, and said, 'Well, that about decides it.'

Bao Renwen also stood up, patted the dirt off his rump, and said, 'Yes, that about decides it.'

'Then let's head along!'

'Yes, let's head along.'

He repeated this mechanically, with no idea of where they wanted to go.

Leaving the wheat field, they climbed into the jeep. Its gassy smell brought him to his senses – they were going to Dregs' house, to have a look at it and to talk to Dregs' parents.

Bao Yanshan's wife was lighting the fire. She scrambled to her feet when she saw two strangers standing at her door. Comrade Wang immediately announced, 'This is a journalist from the regional *Morning Star News*, come to pay a call and inquire about events regarding your Bao Renping. He's going to report on it!'

This did not make Dregs' mother less apprehensive.

'These are county and regional cadres come to ask about Dregs – they want to write an article praising him,' Bao Renwen interpreted.

Then she understood and loosened up, saying, 'Come in, come in.'

The room was pitch black. Stored grain took up one third

of its space. Unused to this kind of living arrangement, Comrade Hu inched inside cautiously, looking all around and not saying a word. Someone was sent down to The Lake to bring home Bao Yanshan.

'This is Bao Renping's father,' Bao Renwen introduced him when he arrived.

The men advanced on him, one grabbed his hand and shook it vigorously. Bao Yanshan looked at them, flustered, and slowly took back his hand.

After each had found a seat, Comrade Hu wiped his glasses for a moment, then began to ask questions in a low and sympathetic voice.

'From what age did Bao Renping start attending to the Five-Guaranteed Grandfather?'

'. . . why, he was a friend of Gramps ever since he was a baby. Soon as he could talk he'd invite him over to eat, soon as he could walk he'd be taking flatbread over to him.'

'And why do you think he was so attentive to Bao Fifth Grandfather?'

'Those two were meant to be together by fate. Gramps didn't pay heed to nobody – stubborn! Oh, was he stubborn. The only one that mattered to him was Dregs.'

'Did Bao Renping ever keep a diary?'

'Diary?'

'When Dregs was alive did he write things down every day?' Bao Renwen explained. Imperceptibly, he had become the interpreter.

'Ever since he started school, when he'd finished class and cut his pig grass and eaten his dinner every day, he'd sit right down at that table and start to write. Write! Why, he would write till in winter his hands were numb with the cold – and then he'd still write. He'd write in summer till the mosquitoes were driving him mad but he'd keep on writing. You'd say to him, "Dregs, you can write it all tomorrow!" And he'd say, "Tomorrow has its own work to do."'

'Do you still have all the things he wrote?'

'Burned them, together with the bookbag.'

'Burned them?' Comrade Hu was astonished.

'It's the custom in this place,' Bao Renwen explained. 'It's not lucky to have the things of little ghosts hanging around the house – you've got to burn them all. What can't be burned has to be buried, or thrown out.'

'Ah.' Comrade Hu drew in a quiet breath.

'This child had a hard life,' his father continued. 'Didn't have a single square meal.' He sighed loudly, and a tear or two dropped onto the floor. Then he cleared his throat, spat twice and used his boot to wipe the phlegm away.

Comrade Hu did not speak. After a moment, he said softly, 'We'll be going.'

Bao Renwen led them to the base of the big willow tree to have a look. Comrade Hu put his head back to look at the branches, wondering how Fifth Grandfather managed to climb to the top. Then he put his head down and looked at the trunk, imagining how Dregs embraced the tree until he was dead. Then he rubbed the rough bark and was quiet for awhile.

Bao Renwen led them to the side of the big ditch where they had put Dregs' grave. Tender green grass was growing on the mound, softly rippling back and forth in the breeze. A lamb was grazing on it, while a child washed his feet in the ditch. At the sight of strangers, the child's eyes widened and he stared.

'Come on over here, little one, there's something I'd like to ask you,' Comrade Wang called to him.

The child scampered up, grabbed the lamb by the neck, turned and ran.

'Children around here don't know much about the outside world,' Bao Renwen apologized for him.

Comrade Wang shook his head and laughed. 'I was just going to ask him about Bao Renping.'

Comrade Hu never said a word, just stood looking down at Dregs' small grave.

The grass on the mound was green and tender, and moved softly under the wind.

CHAPTER 36

Bao Bingde's wife was having her child. Someone went down to The Lake to get Bao Bingde, who bolted back as fast as he could run. Just as he got to the door, before he had time to put down his hoe, a cry came from inside and a new baby slipped easily into the world. It was a fat little girl.

Not a fat little boy – but Bao Bingde could not have cared less. Girls, boys, he wanted them all – to him they were all precious. He had already dreamed many times of somebody calling him Daddy.

It was not two months before his wife was pregnant again. A worker from the Birth Control Office came around, wanting her to have an abortion and then tie her tubes. Bao Bingde gave permission, and the next day took his wife up into the mountains to hide out at her in-laws'. As the saying goes, 'Keep the tree green and you'll still get firewood.'*

---

* In China's countryside, lower branches of trees are cut off for firewood – top branches are left to keep the tree alive. The meaning of the saying is: 'Keep the wife intact and you will still get children.' The practice of hiding pregnant wives, and of having more children than officially allowed, is widespread in China.

Walking back alone he felt deliriously happy. He had not dreamed that a person could be so blessed, especially since the future had looked so grim before. Unexpectedly, the mountain path turned and then ran straight again, and in the darkness he found himself walking along the big ditch. Soon he was approaching the small mound that was Dregs' grave.

The wind sighed across the top of it, and his legs suddenly buckled as he thought of the crazy one. Black water filled the ditch in front of him, and as he knelt a strange thought came to mind: 'Damned if it wasn't Dregs who pulled her off. He could see my life was getting unbearable. Damned if he didn't pull her off for me.'

He looked back at the grave, where the grass shone white in the moon.

'Everybody said this child understood things – so young, and so thoughtful.'

Then he looked again at the ditch and the water, which shot back flashes of the moon.

'Strange, that child . . . and strangely kind. And with a fate so tied to Bao Fifth Grandfather. He truly was a different child.'

He picked up a handful of dirt and pressed it on to the mound.

'Child, let your seventh uncle's daughter grow up to be as good as you!' He patted the earth down firmly, paused a moment, then stood and walked on.

Meanwhile, on the other side of the ditch two figures were talking in the shadow of a tree.

'Your family has harvested so much grain this year – why don't you build a house?'

'My father says we've got to pay the bills first. These past few years – you know yourself how bad they've been – we've come to owe the troop a lot of money. He says you have to be trustworthy to be a man – it won't do not to repay what you've borrowed.'

'So when are you ever going to build a house?'

'When we've harvested the wheat and sold the grain, then we'll build.'

'Why doesn't your family go into business? You're killing yourselves by planting only grain. Plant some cash crops, take them on the streets and make money.'

'My dad says the most important thing is grain. If you've got grain, you don't have to worry about anything else. And he says –'

'What else does he say?'

'He says we're honourable, and our own bosses. We're not the kind to go into business.'

'What's wrong with going into business?'

'You have to trap people in it, lead them on. You have to be cunning before you're any good at it.'

'The streets are full of people doing business these days – are they all wolves?'

'That's not what I mean.'

A stone was tossed into the ditch. The drops from the splash started circles going, one running into another.

'Angry?' he asked.

'What should I be angry about? I'm afraid that to try to build a house you're all going to starve to death. I know you need to eat a lot.'

'The whole earth is covered with things to eat – all the green things and yellow things, like that grass there, or the weeds over there.'

'You eat that and you'll get dropsy. I should know – my father died of dropsy.'

'Wouldn't happen to us. My mother says when we're selling the grain we'll keep some back for ourselves.'

'You'll have to.'

A breeze came up in the small stand of trees. The water in the ditch broke into sparkling ripples under the moon.

'What are you thinking about, Jade?'

'I'm thinking that when I come next time I'll bring you some steamed buns to eat.'

CHAPTER 37

Bao Renwen went with Comrade Hu to the county seat and they stayed together for three days in the Number One Guesthouse. They called it 'cooperation', but in fact it was Bao Renwen putting forth the material and Comrade Hu wielding the pen. After finishing the piece, Comrade Hu handed it over for his co-author to take a look – he wanted to know if there were phrases that did not ring true. Bao Renwen pointed some out and Comrade Hu made corrections, but as before the one used his mouth while the other used the pen. Bao Renwen felt that this way of writing was most unsatisfactory.

These three days with Comrade Hu had at least accomplished one thing: they had shredded that mysterious and special aura he had always thought surrounded journalists. He had not realized that journalists, like him, were human. They needed to eat, they needed to sleep – they also snored. Their snoring, indeed, could be like thunder assaulting your ear: for two nights Bao Renwen hardly slept.

He learned that Comrade Hu was three or four years younger than he, that he had been sent to live and work in a production brigade,* had done self-study, then finally joined the newspaper. Once or twice he invited Bao Renwen to have a drink with him, and when he drank too much he began to tell Bao Renwen his troubles. He was resentful that he did not have a degree, and he was resentful that as a result he felt unpopular. The rooms at the paper were crowded, the pay was low, and the bonus system had still not started. Bao Renwen found it difficult to understand how anyone in such an exalted profession could have so many mundane and trivial problems. He also wondered how anyone with such a diversity of troubles could carry on the work of developing the human spirit.

By the time he set off, walking back home from the county seat, he was filled with a sense of irremediable loss. But when he entered Baotown and found he was the object of a new respect, his soul gradually began to feel replenished.

One week later, the lead article of the *Morning Star News* carried the story: 'A Little Hero Grows Up Under Bao Mountain'. His own name was grandly set out in print, under the headline, right after Comrade Hu's. As he looked at the paper, Renwen's heart began to beat so hard that it seemed to want to jump right out of his throat. He calmed down a little and began to read the article, and slowly his pulse returned to normal. There wasn't a single line in the article that had been written by him. He calmed himself further and read the article through from the top again. This time he discovered that several sentences must have come from his earliest draft. For example, 'Faced with death, he gave life to another and took death for himself': he clearly remembered that sentence from the original manuscript. By the time he had read the article some five or six times, he recognized his own labour between the words and the lines. He was happy to agree that it had indeed been written by both Comrade Hu and himself.

---

* Around 14 million young people were sent to the countryside to work in production brigades during the Cultural Revolution.

At last his name and his article had been set in print. Those printed words were a kind of confirmation. Never again would his name be insignificant – it was as though his existence had been certified, as though he had been made more real. If he had ever had doubts about his actual being, those doubts were gone.

Culture read the article out for his mother, but instead of crying, he found that she was indifferent. It could have been the story of some other family – the words that moved others seemed to have no effect on his parents. The Dregs of the article had been separated from themselves. It was only when his own name was mentioned that Bao Yanshan raised his head, and asked, 'Is that me?'

'Yes, you – you're Dregs' father, after all.'

'No point in bringing me in there – I'm not at all interesting.'

'But you're Dregs' father.'

Then he did not say any more.

The article also mentioned others, among them the mayor, who had organized the rescue, and Picked-Up, who had hauled Dregs out. All of these people had Culture or some other child who was literate read it to them several times.

The piece hit a chord. Many letters were sent to Baotown's school, Dregs' parents and Baotown in general. On the day of Qingming,* the whole school turned out to sweep Dregs' grave. The custom in Baotown was to press handfuls of earth against the mound and to offer wreaths of wildflowers tied together with grasses. The flowers were every colour of the rainbow, and in the sunlight the wreaths looked magnificent.

In two more months the harvest was over, and soon after that another jeep made its way into Baotown. This time it carried three people: Comrade Wang, a woman in a dress and a man of around forty. They marched together into the house

---

* Festival held in spring, to honour the ancestors and the dead.

of Bao Yanshan: this time they were reporters from the provincial authority, which had decided to make a propaganda campaign out of Dregs.

Bao Yanshan was a great deal more assured than the last time. He shook hands, and gracefully asked his guests to take a seat. Then he related the entire story of Dregs' sacrifice, from beginning to end, although this still hurt and by the end he was getting shaky.

'Which heroic person did Bao Renping most respect while he was living?' the woman asked.

Bao Yanshan did not quite grasp her meaning, but was too embarrassed to have things explained to him all the time. He simply nodded his head gravely as he pondered the question, and then replied, 'Dregs was very respectful to both children and adults. When he met an older person he would always give a greeting, and he never had fights or arguments with other children.'

The woman took some time scratching this into her notebook, then asked, 'Whose influence made him behave this way?'

Bao Yanshan again thought for awhile, then said, 'His mother and I always said to him, "When you meet someone older than you are you must never be impolite. With people younger than you, you have to make allowances. That's the way to be a good child." We in Baotown have always paid attention to kindness. If somebody's in trouble, then everybody knows and everybody helps. That is the influence that this child received.'

The woman scratched awhile in her notebook, then raised her head and asked, 'Was taking care of Bao Fifth Grandfather something that the school assigned him to do?'

'No, he just liked Fifth Grandfather. The two of them were fated to be together. The fact is, Fifth Grandfather liked him too – only if both of them liked each other could it work like that.'

The man spoke up then, 'Could we see the bookbag that Bao Renping used while he was alive?'

'It was burned,' Bao Yanshan explained himself this time. 'The custom in Baotown is not to keep the things of little ghosts around the house. Everything that can burn is burned, the rest is buried.'

'Is there a picture of him?' the man asked.

'No, he never saw a camera in his life.'

'Oh.' The man was silenced by that.

'This child had a hard life, never a decent meal to eat.' Bao Yanshan's eyes began to redden as he pointed to the bundles of grain stacked up in the room. 'Now that we have enough to eat, he's not here.' He choked up then, and could not say any more.

'We'll go pay a call on Picked-Up now,' and they all stood up and took their leave.

Bao Yanshan stood in the doorway, watching them go. He thought sadly, 'This child Dregs didn't have much when he lived – now that he's dead there are all these people coming to express concern. I guess that could be counted as a kind of good fortune too.' The thought seemed to give him a little comfort.

He was leaning against the door when he heard a sound: tock tock, tock tock, tock tock. Out on the road, an older person with a pedlar's pole was coming into town.

CHAPTER 38

Picked-Up was lighting the fire in the stove. Second Aunt pushed him away from it as soon as she saw provincial cadres had come to pay a call, and she lit it herself while Picked-Up went to smoke and talk.

'The day it all happened, was it you who pulled Dregs out of the water?' the man asked.

'Everybody went down, not just me. They hauled up some old shoes and a jacket. In the end, I just hauled up Dregs,' Picked-Up said modestly.

'How did you find him?'

'I closed my eyes and dived down hard as I could.' As he said this, Second Aunt carried in several bowls of tea, one for each person. She also had one on the tray for Picked-Up – he hurriedly got up to take the tray, but Second Aunt stepped aside, put the tray on a board, and said, 'It's hot, don't burn yourself.'

He gave her a thankful look and continued his description. 'So I dived down as hard as I could, and my hands hit the old willow trunk. Hanging on to that, I made my way down to the base until I ran into a small hand. I couldn't hold my breath any longer, so I went up for air and then came down again. At first I couldn't budge him — his arms were locked around the trunk in a death grip.'

'Oh.' The man let out a sigh. The woman, without stopping, got everything in her book.

'He died for Bao Fifth Grandfather,' Picked-Up concluded.

Both man and woman were moved. The young woman's eyes were wet and shiny as they looked at Picked-Up. Under her gaze Picked-Up felt his face turn red, and he lowered his head.

'We'll be going along to the mayor now — he was the one who organized the rescue, wasn't he?' the man asked Picked-Up.

'Yes, as soon as he heard somebody was missing, he led us down the mountain.'

'Where does he live?'

'In the eastern part of town — there's a row of . . .'

'Father, why don't you accompany the two cadres and show them how to find it,' Second Aunt spoke up.

Picked-Up looked at Second Aunt, and Second Aunt looked straight back at him. Then he stood up and followed the two of them out.

Not long after this, the provincial newspaper carried a long article with the headline: 'The New Style of Youth. Sacrificing One's Own Interests for the Sake of Others: The Little Hero, Bao Renping'. The article went into lengthy detail and was illustrated. When it was passed around, everyone said the drawing looked exactly like Dregs. It mentioned Picked-Up, and here it got a bit flowery, saying he was 'pure, simple and honest, and had a strapping physique'. It said that he had gone down into the floodwater several times, but when he finally reached Bao Renping, the little hero breathed his last in Picked-Up's arms. It also touched on the matter of Picked-Up and Second Aunt, saying that he took her children as his own, and did not mind that she was poor.

The above was all written as background to how a hero

grows up. It even mentioned the old revolutionary, Bao Yan-rong, and described his glorious history. It said that from birth the hero had grown up in such a place, where his elders had a spirit of self-sacrifice. This doubtless had exerted a subtle influence on the hero.

Bao Yanrong had this particular passage read and reread to him, and he chewed the words over in his mind for quite some time. In the end they stirred up a long-slumbering sense of glory. Several times after that he went looking for Bao Renwen, intending now to try to answer his questions. But Bao Renwen had quit that idea and was working on a magnum opus: he wanted to write a richer, more literary piece, one that chronicled the life of the local hero.

Not long after the article appeared, school students from the neighbouring towns and even the next county began to line up to offer floral wreaths at Dregs' grave. The trips were organized to pay homage to the little hero; the children made solemn oaths, swearing that they would be just like Dregs. Every kind of floral wreath now covered the fresh green grass on the mound – the pile grew until from a distance it looked like a large bouquet.

The provincial publishing house now sent a writer and an editor to Baotown, for the purpose of publishing a book called *The Story of a Little Hero*.

At last Renwen had the chance to see a live author at close range.

He was thin and short, around forty years old, and he smoked heavily. He seemed to have a problem in his throat – it rattled even when the man was not saying anything. After looking over Bao Renwen's manuscript, the author decided they should work together. The 'Story' would be based on the 'Chronicle', for which Bao Renwen had already amassed a large amount of material. Together, they interviewed the little hero's relatives and then they went to look for Picked-Up.

Picked-Up was not at home, but Second Aunt was. Bao Renwen introduced her to the author, saying, 'This is Picked-

133

Up's home-person.' Then he said, 'Picked-Up's home-person, would you go down to The Lake to call Picked-Up to come here and talk to us?'

Off she went.

Bao Renwen then explained to the author, 'In Baotown, when you say "wife" you always say "the home-person" of the husband. I'm telling you so you'll understand the customs around here.' The author smiled.

Picked-Up came home, first greeted the author, and then yelled to his wife, 'Make tea!' She promptly squatted down by the stove to light the wood to begin heating water.

Picked-Up then related once again the sequence of events as he pulled out Dregs. 'I dived down as hard as I could. Nothing. I dived down again, harder. Still nothing. Then I thought to myself, with Bao Fifth Grandfather crouching up in the top of the tree, Dregs would certainly not have gone far from the bottom. So, hugging the tree, I made my way down again, feeling all around the trunk. You know, this tree, in the east, is the highest tree we have in Baotown. That day, the water was covering it so only the very top of the branches showed. Just think, could anything in so much water have possibly sur-
·ived?'

The author nodded his head, and took notes in his book.

'So, holding on to the trunk, I felt my way down, until I suddenly felt a little hand, cold as ice . . .' As he narrated, his voice began to waver as his own description inspired him. Just at that moment, Second Aunt came in bearing the tea.

These days, Second Aunt had become thoroughly respectful to Picked-Up. In fact, the whole town behaved differently towards him now. Even he felt he was not the same person as before. His back was straighter, his steps were wider, he began to relate to other people.

'Picked-Up, did the author eat lunch together with you at your house today?' somebody was curious to know.

'No – they went up to the township to eat.'

'Well, why didn't you have the author to lunch?'

'I asked him, but he was too polite. City folk are polite like that,' Picked-Up explained.

'Picked-Up, how is it you haven't gone back to your old home to have a look?'

'Too far. I won't be going.'

'Is anybody still left in your family?'

'Just me.' Picked-Up's voice dropped to a whisper and you could tell he was hurting inside.

A few days later, somebody brought Picked-Up a message: at the edge of town an old pedlar had been seen walking around. When he saw a person from Baotown, he asked them about Picked-Up – how was he getting along after his marriage –and the person from Baotown answered in full. Just before moving on, the old pedlar asked the person to pass on a message to Picked-Up: his old Aunt was doing all right up in the north. She had enough to eat and she had enough to wear. The person from Baotown asked him, 'Don't you want to come over and visit Picked-Up?' but he answered quietly, 'No, I don't believe so.'

That night Picked-Up had a dream. He dreamed a pedlar's drum kept sounding in his ear: tock tock, tock tock, tock tock.

CHAPTER 39

One day a jeep drove down from the county government office, and stopped in front of Bao Yanshan's door. Out stepped the party secretary of the county. He grabbed Bao Yanshan's hand, and loudly announced, 'The Provincial Committee of the Communist Youth League of China has elected Bao Renping as a Youth Hero! Congratulations on the glorious honour!'

Bao Yanshan was stupefied. His dry tree-branch of a hand was encased in the warm soft hand of the Party Secretary. He was not too clear about the significance of 'Youth Hero', but he knew that to be congratulated by such a man was a very rare thing. He became flustered and could not think of anything to say.

Supporting the arm of the Youth Hero's father, the county secretary entered the home of the Youth Hero. He fell silent, and stayed silent for a long time. Finally, out came the words, 'Hard life, you all.'

'Not so bad now there's plenty of grain.' Bao Yanshan pointed out the bundles of stacked wheat. 'Just that Dregs, he's . . . not here.'

136

'Do you have enough to eat?' The county secretary gingerly touched one of the bundles of grain.

Bao Yanshan's wife quickly interrupted, 'We've been discussing selling the grain, to build a house.'

The secretary raised his head, looked around at the black hole of a room, and said, 'This house won't do.'

'Without a house, our older son – he's twenty-seven – can't find a wife.' She wiped off a tear.

The Secretary again regarded the room, and then said slowly, 'The grain must absolutely not be sold.' He shook Bao Yanshan's hand once more and left.

The next day the mayor of Baotown came to tell Bao Yanshan that the county had allocated lumber, cement and bricks to his family so they could build themselves a house.

In another few days the mayor told Bao Yanshan that the agricultural-machinery factory in the area had put Construction's name on their list, so he could now use their coupons to buy government food.

Exactly one year after Dregs died the county made the decision to move his grave.

Floral wreaths were brought in from the schools of county, region and town.

Dregs' casket was removed from its resting place beside the big ditch and taken to the middle of Baotown. A platform with over a dozen stairs was erected in the town square. On the platform was built a tall monument. On the monument was laid a stone plaque reading:

FOREVERMORE.

The new plaque, not the old willow tree, was now the highest thing in Baotown. It shone proudly in front of the hazy outline of Bao Mountain.

The drums of the troop began to beat, the anthem of the troop rang out, the secretary made a speech and contributed the first wreath . . .

Bao Yanshan and his wife sat in front, in a daze, wanting to cry and yet not daring to shed a tear. A number of people had made it clear to them that, this time, crying would not be appropriate.

Dregs' grave now stood, like a kind of house, in the centre of town. Made of bricks and mortar, it would not be growing any grass, and there would not be lambs coming around to graze on it any more.

CHAPTER 40

The centre beam was raised on Bao Yanshan's house, and it was roofed and gradually finished. Large windows let light into four spacious rooms with whitewashed walls and solid cement floors.

Construction started his job in the agricultural-machinery factory, and found that he was overwhelmed by people wanting to introduce their daughters. It was now his turn to try to avoid them.

On the day Construction was married, Little Jade returned. She came through the door, kneeled before her foster parents and loudly knocked her head on the floor in a kowtow. Before they could recover their senses she had scrambled up to get the water pail. After several trips to the well the two large water jars were brimming over, but she disregarded Culture's protestations and went out for more. He followed her and caught up with her just as she reached the well. She was lowering the bucket when he grabbed for it and it fell into the water. The two of them leaned against the side of the well trying to hook it up.

'Stupid!' Little Jade said.

'Why blame me?' Culture was hurt.

'I can't help blaming you.'

'What do you blame me for?' He was more and more upset.

'Blame you for being number two instead of number one.'

'So what if I were number one? What's wrong with my being number two?'

'If you had been number one, would I have had to go to all this trouble?' Her lips quivered and her eyes began to get moist.

The two of them cried in earnest then, the tears disappearing noiselessly into the depths of the well.

A road was built through town. With the number of vehicles and people increasing daily, the old road was inadequate. It was widened and paved, and to do this they had to cut through Picked-Up's vegetable patch. He and his wife gladly donated the land and refused to take any compensation. Picked-Up said, 'If I were to take money for it, I'd lose my self-respect.'

The county wanted to build a memorial hall in front of Dregs' tomb, but it soon ran into the problem of having none of Dregs' personal items to display. Everything used and worn by the Youth Hero in his lifetime had been burned. At one point Dregs' signature was found on the mud wall of an outhouse. He and a young friend had written their own names, Bao Renping and Bao Yaohe. The friend was asked if he was absolutely sure that this was the handwriting of Bao Renping, and he answered, 'Absolutely. The two of us were taking a shit together and we just wrote our names for fun.'

The trouble was that the mud wall began to crumble as soon as they tried to lift the signature off, so in the end they had to leave the Youth Hero's signature where it was.

EPILOGUE

Dregs' tomb stood high and imposing in the centre of town, and the steps to his tomb were always immaculate. There was no need for the mayor to arrange for anyone to sweep it – many volunteered to do the job. In addition to his mother, father, brothers and sister-in-law, Bao Renwen, Bao Bingde and Picked-Up swept it every few days. The only thing they requested from the mayor was a communal broom – using a family broom to sweep a grave always seemed a little unlucky.

The sun reflected off the plaque, new and so shiny that it hurt the eyes.

Behind the tomb now stood a brand-new brick house with a tiled roof, and behind the house was Bao Mountain, looming in the distance. It seemed shrouded in fog, as though it were far away, but at the same time, though indistinct, it could have been very near.

ANOTHER EPILOGUE

Bao Bingyi was playing a tune and singing:

二 千 'Add a line to "two" and read it "*qian*".
     Qian Gan Luo became Prime Minister at the age of twelve.
一 丁 "One" with a bar and a hook becomes a "*ding*".
     Ding Lang tried his best to be a filial son.

     One two three four five six seven eight nine ten.
     Ten nine eight seven six five four three two one.
     These are some of the pearls of wisdom
     On the bead curtain at the door . . .'

As he listened, Bao Yanrong felt transported. He was remembering the great times that he had been through. When the Captain died, Bao Yanrong had yelled, 'Follow me!' and they had fought until there were only two and a half men left. He wondered where that old war comrade was today, the one who was left with only one arm and one leg.

A solitary man sat on the planks of the bed, hugging his knees. He was an old man, with a rounded back and wrinkled face. A pedlar from far to the north, he was sleeping in the cow-pen for the night. He listened as he sat against the wall, but his two eyes were fixed on Picked-Up sitting in the doorway.

Picked-Up felt the eyes, and turned around to look. He looked once, looked again, and then felt something change inside. When he looked this time, he could not look away. Two pairs of eyes met, and the ballad continued.